Heavenly Highway Hymns

A Choice Collection of Gospel Songs, both Old and New,
Suitable for Religious Work and Worship

Compiled by

L U T H E R   G.   P R E S L E Y

SHAPE NOTES ONLY

Printed in U.S.A.

Limp — 5396

Cloth — 5397

Spiral — 5398

Order from

STAMPS - BAXTER MUSIC
of   the   ZONDERVAN   CORPORATION
P. O. BOX 4007 ● DALLAS, TEXAS 75208

Doxology

No. 00

Thomas Ken

Louis Bourgeois

Praise God from whom all blessings flow, Praise Him all creatures here be-low;

Praise Him a-bove, ye heav'n-ly host, Praise Fa-ther, Son and Ho — ly Ghost.

Revive Us Again

No. 00

Wm. P. Mackay

J. J. Husband

1. We praise Thee, O God! for the Son of Thy love, For Je - sus who
2. We praise Thee, O God! for Thy Spir - it of light, Who has shown us our
3. All glo - ry and praise to the Lamb that was slain, Who has borne all our

died and is now gone a-bove.
Sav-ior and scattered our night. Hal - le - lu - jah! Thine the glo-ry, Hal - le-
sins, and has cleansed ev-'ry stain.

CHORUS

lu - jah! A - men! Hal - le - lu - jah! Thine the glo-ry, Re-vive us a - gain.

No. 1   Higher Ground

Rev. Johnson Oatman, Jr.

Chas. H. Gabriel

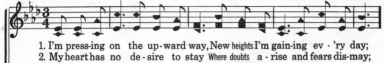

1. I'm press-ing on the up-ward way, New heights I'm gain-ing ev - 'ry day;
2. My heart has no de - sire to stay Where doubts a - rise and fears dis-may;
3. I want to live a - bove the world, Tho' Sa-tan's darts at me are hurled;
4. I want to scale the ut-most height, And catch a gleam of glo - ry bright;

Still pray-ing as I on-ward bound, "Lord, plant my feet on high - er ground."
Tho' some may dwell where these a-bound, My pray'r, my aim is high - er ground.
For faith has caught the joy - ful sound, The song of saints on high - er ground.
But still I'll pray till heav'n I've found, "Lord, lead me on to high - er ground."

CHORUS

Lord, lift me up and let me stand, By faith, on heav-en's ta - ble-land;

A high - er plane than I have found, Lord, plant my feet on high - er ground.

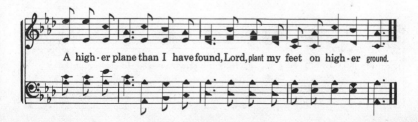

No. 2 Heavenly Sunlight

Rev. H. J. Zelley

G. H. Cook

1. Walk-ing in sun-light, all of my jour-ney; O - ver the moun-tains
2. Shad-ows a-round me, shad-ows a-bove me, Nev-er con-ceal my
3. In the bright sun-light, ev-er re-joic-ing, Press-ing my way to

thru the deep vale; Je - sus has said I'll nev - er for-sake thee,
Sav - ior and Guide; He is the light in Him is no dark-ness,
man-sions a - bove; Sing-ing His prais-es glad - ly I'm walk-ing,

CHORUS

Prom-ise di - vine that nev - er can fail.
Ev - er I'm walk-ing close to His side. Heav-en - ly sun-light,
Walk-ing in sun - light, sun-light of love.

heav-en - ly sun-light; Flood-ing my soul with glo - ry di-vine: Hal - le-

lu - jah, I am re-joic-ing, Sing-ing His prais-es, Je - sus is mine.

No. 3   Glory Hallelujah in My Soul

G. T. BYRD

1. When I came to Christ, I was all de-filed, Now there's glory hal-le-
2. Yes, I came to Christ with my load of sin, There's a glo-ry hal-le-
3. Come, O wan-der-er, come and go with me, There's a glo-ry hal-le-
4. I will hon-or Christ where-so-e'er I go, There's a glo-ry hal-le-
5. When I leave the earth I will say good-by, There's a glo-ry hal-le-

lu-jah in my soul; Since I saw the blood and was rec-on-ciled,
lu-jah in my soul; And I plead and knock'd till He let me in,
lu-jah in my soul; Come and see what Christ's blood will do for thee,
lu-jah in my soul; His blood has wash'd me as white as snow,
lu-jah in my soul; I will soar to-ward heav'n, far above the sky,

REFRAIN

There's a glo-ry hal-le-lu-jah in my soul. There is glo - - ry,
There is glo-ry,

There is glo - - ry, There's a glo-ry hal-le-lu-jah in my soul, There is
There is glo-ry,

glo - - ry, There is glo - ry, There's a glo-ry hal-le-lu-jah in my soul.
There is glory,   There is glory,

No. 4 — He Prayed

E. M. Bartlett

J. M. Henson

1. Je - sus went up - on the moun-tain that He might com - mune with God,
2. All a - lone while in the gar - den where He sweat great drops of blood,
3. When up - on the cross of Cal - v'ry in His ag - o - ny and pain,

He prayed, He prayed; On the hills of old Ju - de - a which my
Not my will but Thine be done, my Fa - ther,
He prayed, He prayed; That the Fa - ther might for - give them whom, the

bless - ed Sav - ior trod, He prayed, He prayed. He prayed, He prayed,
was His prayer to God,
Son of God, had slain, He prayed, He prayed. He prayed, He prayed,

Refrain

Je - sus prayed un - to the Fa - ther ev - 'ry day; From the man - ger to the cross,

Not a moment's time was lost, Je - sus prayed un - to the Fa - ther all the way.

No. 5 He's A Wonderful Savior To Me

Virgil P. Brock

Blanche Kerr Brock

1. I was lost in sin but Je-sus res-cued me, He's a won-der-ful
2. He's a Friend so true, so pa-tient and so kind, He's a won-der-ful
3. He is al-ways near to com-fort and to cheer, He's a won-der-ful
4. Dear-er grows the love of Je-sus day by day, He's a won-der-ful

Sav-ior to me;
I was bound by fear but Je-sus set me free,
Ev-'ry-thing I need in Him I al-ways find,
He for-gives my sins, He dries my ev-'ry tear,
so won-der-ful! Sweet-er is His grace while press-ing on my way,

CHORUS

He's a won-der-ful Sav-ior to me.
so won-der-ful!
For He's a won-der-ful

Sav-ior to me,
won-der-ful!
He's a won-der-ful Sav-ior to me;
won-der-ful!
I was

lost in sin, but Je-sus took me in, He's a won-der-ful Sav-ior to me.

No. 6 He Set Me Free

A. E. B. Albert E. Brumley

1. Once like a bird in pris-on I dwelt, No free-dom from my sor-row I felt, But Je-sus came and lis-tened to me And glo-ry to God, He set me free.

2. Now I am climb-ing high-er each day, Dark-ness of night has drift-ed a-way, My feet are plant-ed on high-er ground And glo-ry to God, I'm home-ward bound.

3. Good-by to sin and things that con-found, Naught of the world shall turn me a-round, Dai-ly I'm work-ing, I'm pray-ing, too, And glo-ry to God, I'm go-ing thru.

Chorus

He set me free, yes, He set me free, He broke the bonds of pris-on for me; I'm glo-ry-bound my Je-sus to see, For glo-ry to God, He set me free.

7 Since He Gave Me This Heart Of Love

L. G. P.   Luther G. Presley

1. I'm re-joic-ing in the Sav-ior ev-'ry moment of the day,
2. I can tell the world the sto-ry how the bless-ed Sav-ior came,
3. Hav-ing changed my way of liv-ing there is glo-ry all a-round,

Since He gave me this heart of love;   On and
this heart of love; I can   How He

D.S.-There is

on we walk to-geth-er in the hal-le-lu-jah way,
took a-way my bur-dens, lift-ed me from sin and shame, Since He
feel the Spir-it mov-ing when He sends the blessing down,

something I can feel that makes me know that God is real,

FINE CHORUS

gave me this heart of love.   Since He gave me this heart of
this heart of love.

love,   Clouds no long-er are dark a-bove;
this heart of love,   are dark a-bove;

D.S.

No. 8   I Want To Be A Worker

L. B.

L. Baltzell

1. I want to be a work-er for the Lord, I want to love and trust His ho-ly word; I want to sing and pray, and be bus-y ev-'ry day
2. I want to be a work-er ev-'ry day, I want to lead the err-ing in the way That leads to heav'n a-bove, where all is peace and love,
3. I want to be a work-er strong and brave, I want to trust in Je-sus' pow'r to save; All who will tru-ly come, shall find a hap-py home
4. I want to be a work-er, help me, Lord, To lead the lost and err-ing to Thy word; That points to joys on high, where plea-sures nev-er die

CHORUS

In the king-dom of the Lord. I will work, I will pray, and pray, pray work and pray In the vine-yard, in the vine-yard of the Lord; of the Lord; I will work I will pray, I will la-bor ev-'ry day In the vine-yard of the Lord.

No. 9 It Is Truly Wonderful

B. E. W.

B. E. Warren

1. He pardoned my transgressions, He sanctified my soul,
2. He keeps me ev'ry moment By trusting in His grace;
3. He brings me thru affliction, He leaves me not alone;
4. He prospers and protects me, His blessings ever flow;
5. He keeps me firm and faithful, His love I do enjoy,
6. There's not a single blessing Which we receive on earth

He honors my confessions, Since by His blood I'm whole.
'Tis thru His blest atonement, That I may see His face.
He's with me in temptation, He keeps me for His own.
He fills me with His glory, He makes me white as snow.
For this I shall be grateful, And live in His employ.
That does not come from heaven, The source of our new birth.

Chorus

It is truly wonderful what the Lord has done! It is
truly wonderful! It is truly wonderful! It is
truly wonderful what the Lord has done! Glory to His name.

I've Anchored in Jesus

L. E. J.

L. E. Jones

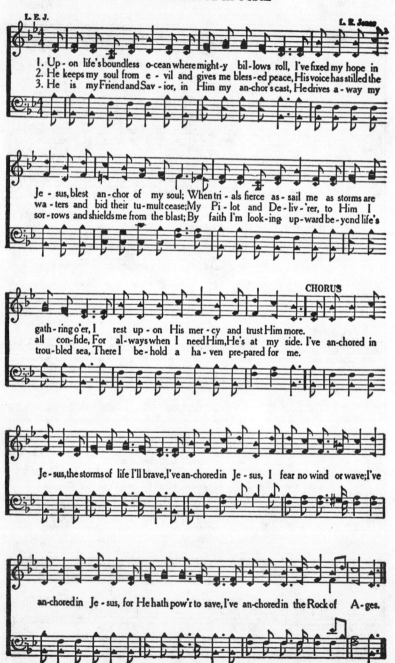

1. Up-on life's boundless o-cean where might-y bil-lows roll, I've fixed my hope in Je-sus, blest an-chor of my soul; When tri-als fierce as-sail me as storms are gath-ring o'er, I rest up-on His mer-cy and trust Him more.

2. He keeps my soul from e-vil and gives me bless-ed peace, His voice has stilled the wa-ters and bid their tu-mult cease; My Pi-lot and De-liv-'rer, to Him I all con-fide, For al-ways when I need Him, He's at my side.

3. He is my Friend and Sav-ior, in Him my an-chor's cast, He drives a-way my sor-rows and shields me from the blast; By faith I'm look-ing up-ward be-yond life's trou-bled sea, There I be-hold a ha-ven pre-pared for me.

CHORUS

I've an-chored in Je-sus, the storms of life I'll brave, I've an-chored in Je-sus, I fear no wind or wave; I've an-chored in Je-sus, for He hath pow'r to save, I've an-chored in the Rock of A-ges.

I'm on the Sunny Side

C. F. W.

C. F. Weigele

1. I've found the Sav-iour, and I'm hap-py now in Him, I'm on the sun-ny side of life; He gives me vic-t'ry, I have peace and joy with-in, I'm on the sun-ny side of life.
2. I've left the wil-der-ness, I'm on the oth-er side, I'm on the sun-ny side of life; Till Je-sus calls me home, in Ca-naan I'll a-bide, I'm on the sun-ny side of life.
3. The pass-ing days bring man-y cares for me, I know, I'm on the sun-ny side of life; I praise the Lord, He keeps me whit-er than the snow, I'm on the sun-ny side of life.
4. Broth-er, so wear-y, hear the Sav-iour call-ing thee, Come on the sun-ny side of life; He will de-liv-er, He will keep thee ev-'ry day, Come on the sun-ny side of life.

CHORUS.

I'm on the sun-ny side, I'm on the sun-ny side, I'm on the sun-ny side of life; I'm on the sun-ny side, I'm on the sun-ny side, I'm on the sun-ny side of life.

No. 12

In The Garden

C. A. M.

C. Austin Miles

1. I come to the gar-den a-lone, While the dew is still on the ros-es; And the voice I hear, Fall-ing on my ear; The Son of God dis-clos-es.

2. He speaks, and the sound of His voice Is so sweet the birds hush their sing-ing, And the mel-o-dy That He gave to me, With-in my heart is ring-ing.

3. I'd stay in the gar-den with Him, Tho' the night a-round me be fall-ing, But He bids me go; Thru the voice of woe, His voice to me is call-ing.

CHORUS

And He walks with me, and He talks with me, And He tells me I am His own, And the joy we share as we tar-ry there, None oth-er has ev-er known.

I Shall Not Be Moved

Arr.

V. O. Fossett

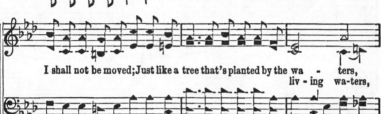

1. Glo - ry hal - le - lu - jah, I shall not be moved; Anchored in Je - ho - vah,
2. In His love a - bid - ing, I shall not be moved; And in Him con - fid - ing,
3. Tho all hell as - sail me, I shall not be moved; Je - sus will not fail me,
4. Tho the tem-pest rag - es, I shall not be moved; On the Rock of A - ges,

I shall not be moved; Just like a tree that's planted by the wa - ters,
liv - ing wa-ters,

Chorus

I shall not be moved. I shall not be, I shall not be

moved, I shall not be, I shall not be moved; Just like a
O glo - ry,

tree that's planted by the wa - - ters, I shall not be moved.
liv - ing wa - ters,

No. 14 — Love Lifted Me

James Rowe   Howard E. Smith

1. I was sink-ing deep in sin, Far from the peace-ful shore, Ver-y
deep-ly stained with-in, Sink-ing to rise no more; But the Mas-ter
of the sea Heard my de-spair-ing cry, From the wa-ters lift-ed me,
Now safe am I.

2. All my heart to Him I give, Ev-er to Him I cling, In His
bless-ed pres-ence live, Ev-er His prais-es sing, Love so might-y
and so true Mer-its my soul's best songs, Faith-ful, lov-ing ser-vice, too,
To Him be-longs.

3. Souls in dan-ger, look a-bove, Je-sus com-plete-ly saves; He will
lift you by His love, Out of the an-gry waves, He's the Mas-ter
of the sea, Bil-lows His will o-bey; He your Sav-ior wants to be—
Be saved to-day.

Chorus

Love lift-ed me! Love lift-ed me!
e-ven me! e-ven me!
When noth-ing else could help, Love lift-ed me; Love lift-ed me.

No. 15 Jesus Is All The World To Me

W. L. T.

Will L. Thompson

1. Je-sus is all the world to me, My life, my joy, my all;
2. Je-sus is all the world to me, My friend in tri-als sore;
3. Je-sus is all the world to me, And true to Him I'll be;
4. Je-sus is all the world to me, I want no bet-ter friend;

He is my strength from day to day, With-out Him I would fall;
I go to Him for bless-ings, and He gives them o'er and o'er;
Oh, how could I this friend de-ny, When He's so true to me?
I trust Him now, I'll trust Him when Life's fleet-ing days shall end;

When I am sad, to Him I go, No oth-er one can cheer me so;
He sends the sun-shine and the rain, He sends the har-vest's gold-en grain;
Fol-low-ing Him I know I'm right, He watch-es o'er me day and night;
Beau-ti-ful life with such a friend; Beau-ti-ful life that has no end;

When I am sad, He makes me glad, He's my friend.
Sun-shine and rain, har-vest of grain, He's my friend.
Fol-low-ing Him, by day and night, He's my friend.
E-ter-nal life, e-ter-nal joy, He's my friend.

No. 16   My Savior First Of All

Fanny J. Crosby

Jno. R. Sweney

1. When my life-work is end-ed, And I cross the swell-ing tide, When the
2. Oh the soul-thrill-ing rap-ture When I view His bless-ed face, And the
3. Oh the dear ones in glo-ry, How they beck-on me to come, And our
4. Thro' the gates to the cit-y In a robe of spot-less white, He will

bright and glo-rious morn-ing I shall see; I shall know my Re-deem-er When I
lus-tre of His kind-ly, beam-ing eye; How my full heart will praise Him For the
part-ing at the riv-er I re-call; To the sweet vales of E-den they will
lead me where no tears shall ev-er fall; In the glad song of a-ges I shall

reach the oth-er side, And His smile will be the first to wel-come me.
mer-cy, love and grace, That prepares for me a man-sion in the sky.
sing my wel-come home, But I long to meet my Sav-iour first of all.
min-gle with de-light; But I long to meet my Sav-iour first of all.

Chorus

I shall know Him, I shall know Him, As re-deemed by His side I shall stand,
I shall know Him,

I shall know Him, I shall know Him By the print of the nails in His hand.
I shall know

No. 17 He'll Understand And Say Well Done

L. E. C.

Lucy E. Campbell
J. R. Baxter, Jr.

Not too fast

1. If when you give the best of your ser-vice, Tell-ing the world that the
2. Mis-un-der-stood, the Sav-ior of sin-ners Hung on the cross, He was
3. When the short life of la-bor is end-ed, Comes the re-ward for the
4. But if you try and fail in the try-ing, With your hands scarred from the

Sav-ior is come; Be not dis-mayed when men don't be-lieve you,
God's on-ly Son, Meek-ly He called His Fa-ther in heav-en,
race you have run, Sweet is the rest pre-pared for the faith-ful,
work you've be-gun; Take up your cross, run quick-ly to meet Him,

CHORUS

He'll un-der-stand and say well done. When you have come to the end of your

jour-ney, Wea-ry of life and the bat-tle you've won, Bear-ing your

staff and the cross of re-demp-tion, He'll un-der-stand and say well done.

Help Somebody Today

Mrs. Frank A. Breck

Chas. H. Gabriel

1. Look all a-round you, find some one in need, Help some-bod-y to-day!
2. Man - y are wait-ing a kind, lov-ing word, Help some-bod-y to-day!
3. Man - y have burdens too heav-y to bear, Help some-bod-y to-day!
4. Some are dis-cour-aged and wea - ry in heart, Help some-bod-y to-day!

Tho' it be lit - tle— a neigh-bor - ly deed, Help some-bod-y to-day!
Thou hast a mes-sage, O let it be heard, Help some-bod-y to-day!
Grief is the por - tion of some ev - 'ry-where, Help some-bod-y to-day!
Some one the jour-ney to heav-en should start, Help some-bod-y to-day!

CHORUS

Help some-bod - y to-day, Some-bod - y a - long life's way; Let
to - day, home - ward way;

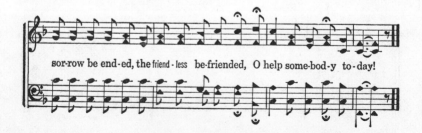

sor-row be end-ed, the friend - less be-friended, O help some-bod-y to-day!

No. 19 Just A Closer Walk With Thee

Copyright, 1948, by Stamps-Baxter Music & Printing Co.
in "Peaceful Echoes"

Anon.   J. R. Baxter, Jr.

1. I am weak but Thou art strong, Je-sus keep me from all
2. Thru this world of toils and snares, If I fal-ter, Lord, who
3. When my fee-ble life is o'er, Time for me will be no

1. I am weak but Thou art strong, Je-sus keep me

wrong; I'll be sat-is-fied as long As I
cares? Who with me my bur-den shares? Let me
more, Guide me to that peace-ful shore, Let me

from all wrong; I'll be sat - is - fied as long As I

CHORUS

walk close to Thee. Just a clos-er walk with Thee,
dear Lord, Just a clos - er, a clos-er walk with Thee,

walk close to Thee.

Grant it, Je-sus, this my plea; Dai-ly let it ev-er
Grant it, Je - sus, this my hum-ble plea; Dai-ly let it, O

be Just a clos - er walk with Thee.
let it ev-er be clos-er walk, just a clos-er walk with Thee.

I Want to Love Him More

W. M. York   Willie York

1. With Je - sus I would ev - er be, His match-less name a - dore;
2. He died up - on the cru - el tree, Our load of guilt He bore;
3. His chil - dren He will not for - sake, When trou-bles press them sore;
4. O Prince of life, sweet Prince of peace, Who dwelt on earth be - low;

He's done so ver - y much for me, I want to love Him more.
He suf - fered shame for you and me, I want to love Him more.
But in their souls sweet peace a - wakes, I want to love Him more.
My faith in Him will nev - er cease, I want to love Him more.

Chorus

I want to love Him more, I want to love Him more; I want to love Him more, I do, I do, I do; I want to love Him more,

I want to love Him more, He's done so much for me, for me.

No. 21   I Am Thine, O Lord

Frances Jane Van Alstyne   W. H. Doane

1. I am Thine, O Lord; I have heard Thy voice, And it told Thy
2. Con-se-crate me now to Thy ser-vice, Lord, By the pow'r of
3. O the pure de-light of a sin-gle hour That be-fore Thy
4. There are depths of love that I can-not know Till I cross the

love to me, But I long to rise in the arms of faith,
grace di-vine; Let my soul look up with a stead-fast hope,
throne I spend, When I kneel in prayer, and with Thee, my God,
nar-row sea; There are heights of joy that I may not reach

CHORUS

And be clos-er drawn to Thee. Draw me near-er,
And my will be lost in Thine.
I com-mune as friend with friend.
Till I rest in peace with Thee.   near-er, near-er,

near-er, bless-ed Lord, To the cross where Thou hast died, Draw me near-er,

near-er, near-er, bless-ed Lord, To Thy pre-cious bleed-ing side.

No. 22 On Jordan's Stormy Banks

Rev. Samuel Stennett

T. C. O'Kane

1. On Jor-dan's storm-y banks I stand, And cast a wish-ful eye
2. O'er all those wide ex-tend-ed plains Shines one e-ter-nal day;
3. When shall I reach that hap-py place, And be for-ev-er blest?
4. Filled with de-light, my rap-tured soul Would here no long-er stay;

To Ca-naan's fair and hap-py land, Where my pos-ses-sions lie.
There God the Son for-ev-er reigns, And scat-ters night a-way.
When shall I see my Fa-ther's face, And in His bos-om rest?
Tho Jor-dan's waves a-round me roll, Fear-less I'd launch a-way.

CHORUS

We will rest in the fair and hap-py land, Just a-
by and by,

cross on the ev-er-green shore, Sing the song of
ev-er-green shore,

Mo-ses and the Lamb, by and by, And dwell with Je-sus ev-er-more.

No. 23 O Happy Day

Philip Doddridge

E. F. Rimbault

1. O hap-py day that fixed my choice On Thee, my Sav-ior and my God!
2. O hap-py bond, that seals my vows To Him who mer-its all my love!
3. 'Tis done; the great trans-ac-tion's done! I am my Lord's and He is mine;
4. High Heav'n, that heard the sol-emn vow, That vow re-newed shall dai-ly hear,

Well may this glow-ing heart re-joice, And tell its rap-tures all a-broad.
Let cheer-ful an-thems fill His house, While to that sa-cred shrine I move.
He drew me, and I fol-lowed on, Charmed to con-fess the voice di-vine.
Till in life's lat-est hour I bow. And bless in death a bond so dear.

Chorus

Hap-py day, hap-py day, When Je-sus washed my sins a-way;

He taught me how to watch and pray, And live re-joic-ing ev-'ry day,

Hap-py day, hap-py day, When Je-sus washed my sins a-way. A-men.

No. 24 O Say, But I'm Glad

Rev. James P. Sullivan

Mildred Ellen Sullivan

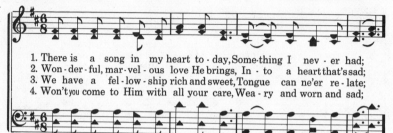

1. There is a song in my heart to-day, Some-thing I nev-er had;
2. Won-der-ful, mar-vel-ous love He brings, In-to a heart that's sad;
3. We have a fel-low-ship rich and sweet, Tongue can ne'er re-late;
4. Won't you come to Him with all your care, Wea-ry and worn and sad;

Je-sus has tak-en my sins a-way, O say, but I'm glad!
Thru dark-est tun-nels the soul just sings, O say, but I'm glad!
Liv-ing in Him is a bless-ed treat, O say, but I'm glad!
You, too, will sing as His love you share, O say, but I'm glad!

CHORUS

O say, but I'm glad, I'm glad, O say, but I'm glad!

Je-sus has come and my cup's o-ver-run, O say, but I'm glad!

No. 25 I'll Live On

T. J. L.

Thos. J. Laney

1. 'Tis a sweet and glo-rious tho't that comes to me, I'll live on,
2. When my bod-y's slumb'ring in the cold, cold clay,
3. When the world's on fire and darkness veils the sun,
4. In the glo-ry-land, with God up-on the throne, I'll live on,

yes, I'll live on; Jesus saved my soul from death and now I'm free,
yes, I'll live on; There to sleep in Je-sus till the judg-ment day,
yes, I'll live on; Men will cry and to the rocks and mountains run,
yes, I'll live on; Thru e-ter-nal a-ges sing-ing, home, sweet home,

CHORUS

I'll live on, yes, I'll live on. I'll live on, yes, I'll live
I'll live on, and on,

on, Thru e-ter-ni-ty I'll live on, I'll live on,
and on, and on, and on,

yes, I'll live on, Thru e-ter-ni-ty I'll live on.
and on, yes, I'll live on.

No. 26   On The Battle Field

Arr.   V. O. Fossett

1. I once was lone and i-dle, I was a sin-ner too,
2. I lost my flag and ban-ner, my staff is in my hand,
3. I'm fight-ing for the king-dom, the bat-tle must be won,

I hear a voice from heav-en, say-ing there is work to do;
I'm tak-ing it to Je-sus, o-ver in the glo-ry land;
The trum-pet will be sound-ing for the com-ing of the Son;

I took my Mas-ter's hand and joined that heav-'nly band, Now I'm
O'er rough ways I have trod, called men to come to God, Now I'm
I'll lay my ar-mor down, take up my robe and crown, Then I'll

D.S.—I prom-ised Him that I would serve Him till I die, So I'm

Fine   **Chorus**

on the bat-tle field for my Lord.   O I'm on the bat-tle field
on the bat-tle field for my Lord.
walk the streets of gold with my Lord.   **for my**

on the bat-tle field for my Lord.

D.S.

for my Lord, Yes, I'm on the bat-tle field for my Lord;

Lord,   **for my Lord;**

No. 27 Mansion Over The Hilltop

I. S.

Ira Stanphill

1. I'm sat - is - fied with just a cot-tage be-low, A lit - tle sil - ver
2. Tho oft - en tempt-ed, tor - ment-ed and test-ed, And like the proph-et
3. Don't think me poor or de - sert-ed or lone-ly, I'm not dis-cour-aged,

and a lit - tle gold; But in that ci - ty where the ran - somed will shine,
my pil-low a stone; And tho I find here no per - ma-nent dwell - ing,
I'm heav - en bound; I'm just a pil-grim in search of a cit - y,

Chorus

I want a gold one that's sil - ver lined.
I know He'll give me a man-sion my own.   I've got a man-sion just
I want a man-sion, a harp and a crown.

o - ver the hill-top, In that bright land where we'll nev - er grow old; And some day

yon-der we will nev - er-more wan - der But walk the streets that are pur-est gold.

This song may be purchased in sheet form at 25 cents from Hymntime Publishers Box 44, Fort Worth, Texas.

Bringing In the Sheaves

GEO. A. MINOR

1. Sow- ing in the morning, sow-ing seeds of kindness, Sowing in the noontide
2. Sow- ing in the sunshine, sow-ing in the shadows, Fearing neither clouds nor
3. Go-ing forth with weeping, sow-ing for the Mas- ter, Tho' the loss sustain'd our

and the dew - y eve; Wait- ing for the har-vest, and the time of reap- ing,
winter's chilling breeze; By and by the har-vest, and the la - bor end - ed,
spir - it oft-en grieves; When our weeping's o - ver, He will bid us wel-come,

REFRAIN.

We shall come re-joic-ing, bringing in the sheaves. Bringing in the sheaves, Bringing
We shall come re-joic-ing, bringing in the sheaves.
We shall come re-joic-ing, bringing in the sheaves. Bringing in the sheaves, Bringing

in the sheaves, We shall come re-joic-ing, Bringing in the sheaves. Bringing in the

sheaves, Bringing in the sheaves, We shall come re-joic-ing, Bringing in the sheaves.

29 Bearing The Cross To Win The Crown

F. R.　　　　　　　　　　　　　　　　　　　　　　　　Fred Rich

1. I'm just a pil-grim passing thru this dark land, of sor-row, Noth-ing but
2. Oft-en my soul is burdened heav-y with care, and trou-ble, Sa-tan oft
3. Must Je-sus bear the cross and let us go free, for ev-er Un-til the

trou-ble have I found; O Lord I need Thy light to guide me a-right,
tries to turn me round; But I'll keep walk-ing in the straight narrow way,
sun of life goes down; No, there's a cross for you and there's one for me,

Fine Chorus

for I am
for I am Bear-ing the cross to win the crown.　Bear-ing the cross
yes, I am

D.S.—for I am Bear-ing the cross to win the crown.

bear-ing the cross,　　　Bear-ing the cross to win the
O Lord I'm　　　　　　yes, I am

D.S.

crown;　　　I need Thy light　　guide me a-right,
in heav-en,　　　of love to

Joy Unspeakable

1 Pet. 1:8

B. E. W.   B. E. Warren

Lively

1. I have found His grace is all com-plete, He sup-pli-eth ev-'ry need;
2. I have found the pleas-ure I once craved, It is joy and peace with-in;
3. I have found that hope so bright and clear, Liv-ing in the realms of grace;
4. I have found the joy no tongue can tell, How its waves of glo-ry roll!

While I sit and learn at Je-sus' feet, I am free, yes, free in-deed..........
What a won-drous bless-ing! I am saved From the aw-ful gulf of sin...........
Oh, the Sav-ior's presence is so near, I can see His smil-ing face.........
It is like a great o'er-flow-ing well, Spring-ing up with-in my soul. ....

CHORUS

It is joy un-speak-a-ble and full of glo-ry, Full of

glo-ry, full of glo-ry, It is joy un-speak-a-ble and

full of glo-ry, Oh, the half has nev-er yet been told.

No. 31 Won't It Be Wonderful There?

James Rowe — Homer F. Morris

1. When with the Sav-ior we en-ter the glo-ry-land, Won't it be
2. Walk-ing and talk-ing with Christ, the su-per-nal One, Won't it be
3. There where the tem-pest will nev-er be sweeping us, Won't it be

won-der-ful there? End-ed the trou-bles and cares of the sto-ry-land,
won-der-ful there? Prais-ing, a-dor-ing the matchless e-ter-nal One,
won-der-ful there? Sure that for-ev-er the Lord will be keeping us,

CHORUS

Won't it be won-der-ful there? Won't it be won-der-ful there,
wonder-ful there,

Hav-ing no bur-dens to bear? Joy-ous-ly sing-ing with
o-ver there?

heart-bells all ring-ing, O won't it be won-der-ful there?
won-der-ful there?

I'll Be List'ning

No. 32

V. O. Stamps

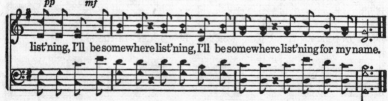

1. When the Sav-ior calls I will an-swer, When He calls for me I will hear; When the Sav-ior calls I will an-swer, I'll be some-where list'ning for my name.

2. If my heart is right when He calls me, If my heart is right I will hear; If my heart is right when He calls me, I'll be some-where list'ning for my name.

3. If my robe is white when He calls me, If my robe is white I will hear; If my robe is white when He calls me, I'll be some-where list'ning for my name.

CHORUS

I'll be somewhere list'ning, I'll be somewhere list'ning, I'll be somewhere list'ning for my name; yes, for my name; I'll be somewhere list'ning, I'll be somewhere list'ning, I'll be somewhere list'ning for my name.

No. 33   Onward, Christian Soldiers

Sabine Gould

A. S. Sullivan

1. On-ward, Chris-tian sol - diers, March-ing as to war, With the cross of
2. At the sign of tri - umph Sa-tan's host doth flee; On, then, Chris-tian
3. Like a might-y ar - my, Moves the Church of God; Broth-ers, we are
4. On-ward, then, ye peo - ple, Join our hap-py throng; Blend with ours your

Je - sus Go - ing on be - fore; Christ, the roy - al Mas - ter,
sol - diers, On - to vic - to - ry! Hell's foun - da - tions quiv - er
tread - ing Where the saints have trod; We are not di - vid - ed,
voic - es In the tri-umph song; Glo - ry, laud and hon - or,

Leads a-gainst the foe; For-ward in - to bat - tle, See, His ban-ners go.
At the shout of praise; Broth-ers, lift your voic - es Loud your an-thems raise!
All one bod - y we, One in hope and doc - trine, One in char - i - ty.
Un - to Christ the King; This thru count-less a - ges, Men and an - gels sing.

CHORUS

On - ward, Chris-tian sol - - diers, March-ing as to

war, With the cross of Je - sus, Go - ing on be - fore.

No. 34   Sunshine in the Soul

E. E. Hewitt   Jno. R. Sweney

1. There's sun-shine in my soul to-day, More glo-ri-ous and bright
2. There's mu-sic in my soul to-day, A car-ol to the King,
3. There's spring-time in my soul to-day, For, when the Lord is near,
4. There's glad-ness in my soul to-day, And hope, and praise, and love,

Than glows in an-y earth-ly skies, For Je-sus is my light.
And Je-sus, lis-ten-ing, can hear The songs I can-not sing.
The dove of peace sings in my heart, The flow'rs of grace ap-pear.
For bless-ings which He gives me now, For joys "laid up" a-bove.

Chorus

O there's sun - - - shine, bless - ed sun - - - shine,
O there's sun-shine in the soul, bless - ed sun-shine in the soul,

When the peace-ful hap-py mo-ments roll;
hap-py mo-ments roll;

When Je-sus shows His smil-ing face, There is sun-shine in the soul.

No.35   Hilltops Of Glory

L. G. P.   Luther G. Presley

1. Once I was bur-dened, my cross so heav - y, And ev - 'ry mo-ment seemed
2. Now I'm re - joic - ing be-cause I love Him, He gives me sun-shine a-
3. Tho I am just a poor earth-ly strang-er, He nev - er leaves me to

fraught with care; I saw my Sav - ior on Calv'-ry's Moun-tain, O hap - py
bove my head; And when temp-ta-tions would o - ver-take me, By His own
walk a - lone; And He has prom-ised when I reach heav-en, I'll have a

CHORUS

day when I met Him there.
hand I am safe - ly led.   Hill-tops of glo - ry where Je-sus is wait-ing,
man-sion, my ver - y own.

'Twas there He met Mo - ses and E - li - jah one day; I came con-fess - ing,

He gave the bless-ing, On the hills of glo - ry, Lord let me stay.

No. 36 The Old Rugged Cross

G. B.

Rev. Geo. Bennard

Solo and Chorus

1. On a hill far a-way stood an old rug-ged cross, The em-blem of
2. Oh, that old rug-ged cross, so de-spised by the world, Has a wondrous at-
3. In the old rug-ged cross, stained with blood so di-vine, A won-drous
4. To the old rug-ged cross, I will ev-er be true, Its shame and re-

suf-f'ring and shame, And I love that old cross where the dear-est and best,
trac-tion for me, For the dear Lamb of God left His glo-ry a-bove,
beau-ty I see; For 'twas on that old cross Je-sus suf-fered and died,
proach glad-ly bear; Then He'll call me some day to my home far a-way,

CHORUS

For a world of lost sin-ners was slain. So I'll cher-ish the old rug-ged
To bear it to dark Cal-va-ry.
To par-don and sanc-ti-fy me.
Where His glo-ry for-ev-er I'll share. cross, the

cross, Till my tro-phies at last I lay down; I will cling to the
old rug-ged cross,

old rug-ged cross, And ex-change it some day for a crown.
cross, the old rug-ged cross,

Standing On The Promises

R. K. C.

R. Kelso Carter

1. Stand-ing on the prom-is-es of Christ my King, Thru e-ter-nal
2. Stand-ing on the prom-is-es that can-not fail, When the howl-ing
3. Stand-ing on the prom-is-es I now can see, Per-fect, pres-ent
4. Stand-ing on the prom-is-es of Christ the Lord, Bound to Him e-
5. Stand-ing on the prom-is-es I can-not fall, List-'ning ev-'ry

a ges let His prais-es ring, Glo-ry in the high-est, I will shout and sing,
storms of doubt and fear as-sail, By the liv-ing Word of God I shall pre-vail,
cleans-ing in the blood for me; Stand-ing in the lib-er-ty where Christ makes free,
ter-nal-ly by love's strong cord, O-ver-com-ing dai-ly with the spir-it's sword,
mo-ment to the Spir-it's call, Rest-ing in my Sav-ior, as my all in all,

CHORUS

Stand-ing on the prom-is-es of God. Stand - ing, stand ing,
Stand-ing on the prom-is-es, stand-ing on the prom-is-es,

Stand-ing on the prom-is-es of God, my Sav-ior, Stand - - ing,
Stand-ing on the prom-is-es,

stand - - - ing, I'm stand-ing on the prom-is-es of God.
stand-ing on the prom-is-es,

No. 38 The Old Gospel Ship

Arr. Alphus LeFevre

1. I have good news to bring and that is why I sing, All my joys with you
2. O I can scarce-ly wait I know I'll not be late, For I'll spend my time
3. If you're ashamed of me you have no cause to be, For with Christ I am

I'll share; I'm going to take a trip in the Old Gos-pel ship
in pray'r; And when my ship comes in I will leave this world of sin
an heir; If too much fault you find you will sure be left be-hind

Chorus

And go sail-ing thru the air.
And go sail-ing thru the air.
While I go sail-ing thru the air. O I'm "gonna" take a trip, in the

good Old Gospel Ship, I'm go-ing far be-yond the sky; O I'm "gonna"

shout and sing un-til the heavens ring, When I'm bidding this world good-bye.

The Last Mile Of The Way

Johnson Oatman, Jr.   Wm. Edie Marks

1. If I walk in the path-way of du-ty, If I work till the
2. If for Christ I pro-claim the glad sto-ry, If I seek for His
3. Here the dear-est of ties we must sev-er, Tears of sor-row are
4. And if here I have earn-est-ly striv-en And have tried all His

close of the day, I shall see the great King in His beau-ty
sheep gone a-stray, I am sure He will show me His glo-ry
seen ev-'ry day; But no sick-ness, no sigh-ing for-ev-er
will to o-bey, 'Twill en-hance all the rap-ture of heav-en

FINE **CHORUS**

When I've gone the last mile of the way. When I've gone the last

mile of the way,   I will rest at the close of the
the last mile of the way,   at the

D.S.

day,   And I know there are joys that a-wait me
close of the day,

No. 40 Hide Me, Rock Of Ages

Copyright 1946 by O. A. Parris in "Charming Refuge"
Assigned 1947 to Stamps Quartet Music Co.

B. C. G.

Brantley C. George

1. O thou bless-ed Rock of A-ges, (Rock of A-ges, I am) Trusting now dear Lord in Thee; (dear Lord in Thee I'm trust-ing) Keep me till my journey's end-ed, (journey's end-ed, Keep me) Till Thy bless-ed face I see.
2. Keep me when the storm-clouds gath-er, (storm-clouds gath-er, keep me) Till the sun comes shin-ing thru; (comes shin-ing thru the shad-ows) Keep me till my work is o-ver, (work is o-ver, Keep me) Till I bid this world a-dieu.
3. When my jour-ney is com-plet-ed, (is com-plet-ed, Sav-ior) And there's no more work to do; (no work to do, O bless-ed) Sav-ior guide my wea-ry spir-it, (wea-ry spir-it, To that) Hap-py land be-yond the blue.

D. S. - When the storm a-round me rag-es, (round me rag-es, Bless-ed) Rock of A-ges hide Thou me.

FINE

CHORUS

Hide me, O blest Rock of A - - ges, A-ges, Rock of A-ges, hide me,

Till Thy bless-ed face I see; (Thy face I see, in glo-ry)

D. S.

No. 41 The Beautiful Garden Of Prayer

Eleanor Allen Scroll

J. H. Fillmore

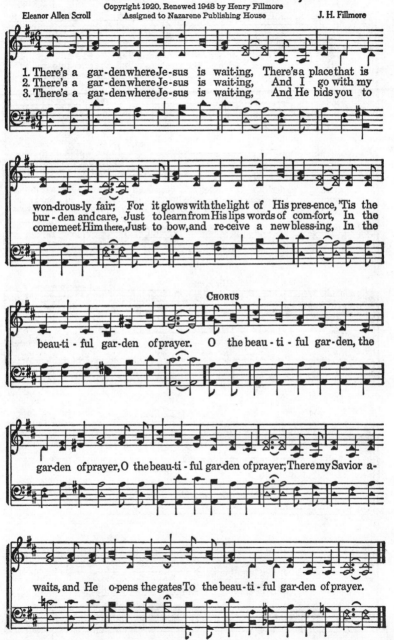

1. There's a gar-den where Je-sus is wait-ing, There's a place that is won-drous-ly fair; For it glows with the light of His pres-ence, 'Tis the beau-ti-ful gar-den of prayer.

2. There's a gar-den where Je-sus is wait-ing, And I go with my bur-den and care, Just to learn from His lips words of com-fort, In the beau-ti-ful gar-den of prayer.

3. There's a gar-den where Je-sus is wait-ing, And He bids you to come meet Him there, Just to bow, and re-ceive a new bless-ing, In the beau-ti-ful gar-den of prayer.

CHORUS

O the beau-ti-ful gar-den, the gar-den of prayer, O the beau-ti-ful gar-den of prayer; There my Savior a-waits, and He o-pens the gates To the beau-ti-ful gar-den of prayer.

No. 42 Tell The Sweet Story Again

J. P. L.

J. P. Lane

1. Je - sus has died, lost sin - ners to save, Tell the sweet sto - ry a-
2. He has redeemed, and paid the great cost, Tell the sweet sto - ry a-
3. Je - sus has bro't sal - va - tion by grace, Tell the sweet sto - ry a-

gain! Died on the cross, and rose from the grave, Tell the sweet
gain! Par - don and life He brings to the lost, Tell the sweet
gain! Ta - ken our sins, and died in our place, Tell the sweet

CHORUS

sto - ry a - gain! Tell the sweet sto - ry a - gain!
and a - gain!

Tell the sweet sto - ry a - gain! Je - sus a-
and a - gain!

lone for sin did a - tone, Tell the sweet sto - ry a - gain!

No. 43   Victory Ahead

W. G.

Rev. William Grum

1. When the hosts of Is - ra - el, led by God, Round the walls of Jer - i - cho
2. Dav - id, with a shep-herd's sling and five stones, Met the gi - ant on the field
3. Dan - iel prayed un - to the Lord thrice each day, Then un - to the li - on's den
4. Oft - en with the car - nal mind I was tried, Ask-ing for de - liv - er-ance
5. When like those who've gone be - fore to that land, By death's riv - er cold and dark

soft - ly trod; Trust-ing in the Lord, they felt the conq'ror's tread, By faith they
all a - lone; Trust-ing in the Lord, he knew what God had said, By faith he
led the way; Trust-ing in the Lord, he did not fear or dread, By faith he
oft I cried, Trust-ing in the Lord, I reck-on'd I was dead, By faith I
I shall stand; Trust-ing in the Lord, I will not fear or dread, By faith I

CHORUS

saw the vic - to - ry a - head.
saw the vic - to - ry a - head.
saw the vic - to - ry a - head. Vic - to - ry a - head! Vic - to - ry a - head!
saw the vic - to - ry a - head.
saw the vic - to - ry a - head.

Thru the blood of Je - sus, vic - to - ry a - head; Trust-ing in the Lord, I

hear the conq'ror's tread, By faith I see the vic - to - ry a - head.

No. 44 When We All Get To Heaven

Mrs. J. G. W.

Mrs. J. G. Wilson

1. Sing the won-drous love of Je - sus, Sing His mer - cy and His grace;
2. While we walk the pil - grim path-way, Clouds will o - ver-spread the sky;
3. Let us then be true and faith-ful, Trust-ing, serv - ing ev - 'ry day;
4. On - ward to the prize be - fore us! Soon His beau - ty we'll be - hold;

In the man-sions, bright and bless-ed, He'll pre-pare for us a place.
But when trav-'ling days are o - ver Not a shad-ow, not a sigh.
Just one glimpse of Him in glo - ry Will the toils of life re - pay.
Soon the pear - ly gates will o - pen, We shall tread the streets of gold.

for us a place.

Chorus

When we all get to heav - en, What a day of re-
When we all What a

joic - ing that will be! When we all see
day of re - joic - ing that will be! When we all

Je - sus, We'll sing and shout the vic - to - ry.
and shout the vic - to - ry.

No. 45 When The Saints Go Marching In

Luther G. Presley   Virgil O. Stamps

1. I'm just a wea-ry pil-grim, Plod-ding thru this world of sin;
2. My fa-ther loved the Sav-ior, What a sol-dier he had been!
3. And moth-er, may God bless her, I can see her now, as then;
4. Up there I'll see the Sav-ior Who redeemed my soul from sin,

Get-ting read-y for that ci-ty When the saints go march-ing in.
But his steps will be more stead-y
With a robe of white a-round her
With ex-tend-ed hands He'll greet me   Saints go march-ing

CHORUS

When the saints   go marching in,   When the saints go
When the saints   marching in,   Saints go

march-ing in;   Lord I want to be in that
march-ing   go marching in O

num-ber   When the saints go march-ing in.
that number,   Saints go march-ing   go march-ing in.

count-less number,

No. 46 When The Savior Reached Down For Me

G.E.W.

G. E. Wright

1. Once my soul was a-stray from the heav-en-ly way, And was wretch-ed and
2. I was near to de-spair when He came to me there, And He showed me that
3. How my heart does re-joice when I hear His sweet voice In the tem-pest, to

vile as could be; But my Sav-ior in love gave me peace from a-bove
I could be free; Then He lift-ed my feet, gave me glad-ness com-plete,
Him I then flee, There to lean on His arm, safe, se-cure from all harm,

CHORUS

1-2 When He reached down His hand for me. When my Sav-ior reached down for
3 Since He for me.

me, When my Sav-ior reached down for me; I was lost and un-
for me, for me;

done, with-out God or His Son, When my Sav-ior reached down for me.
for me.

No. 47 When All Of God's Singers Get Home

Luther G. Presley
Cho. V. O. S.

Virgil O. Stamps

1. What a song of de-light in that ci - ty so bright Will be waft-ed 'neath
2. As we sing here on earth, songs of sadness or mirth, 'Tis a foretaste of
3. Hav-ing o - ver-come sin, "hal - le - lu-jah a-men" Will be heard in that

heav-en's fair dome, How the ransomed will raise hap-py songs in His praise,
rap - ture to come; But our joy can't compare with the glo - ry up there,
land o'er the foam, Ev - 'ry heart will be light and each face will be bright,

CHORUS

When all of God's singers get home. When all of God's singers get home,
When all of God's singers get home,

Where nev - er a sor-row will come; There'll be "no
or heartaches will come; There'll be no

place like home," When all of God's singers get home.
place like heav-en my home, God's singers get home.

No. 48 — When The Battle's Over

Isaac Watts, D.D.

English. Arr. by Wm. B. Blake

1. { Am I a soldier of the cross, A follower of the Lamb.
   { And shall I fear to own His cause, Or blush to speak His name? }
2. { Must I be carried to the skies On flowery beds of ease,
   { While others fought to win the prize, And sailed thro' bloody seas? }
3. { Sure I must fight if I would reign, Increase my courage, Lord;
   { I'll bear the toil, endure the pain, Supported by Thy Word. }

Chorus

And when the battle's over we shall wear a crown! Yes, we shall wear a crown! Yes, we shall wear a crown! And when the battle's over we shall wear a crown In the new Jerusalem.

Wear a crown, wear a crown, Wear a bright and shining crown;
Wear a crown, wear a crown,

When I See The Blood

Foote Bros., not copyrighted. Let no one do so. May this song ever
be free to be published for the glory of God.

John

J. G. F.

1. Christ, our Re - deem - er, died on the cross, Died for the sin - ner,
2. Chief - est of sin - ners Je - sus can save, As He has prom - ised,
3. Judg - ment is com - ing, all will be there, Who have re - ject - ed,
4. O what com - pas - sion, O bound - less love, Je - sus hath pow - er,

paid all his due; All who re - ceive Him need nev - er fear,
so will He do; O sin - ner, hear Him, trust in His word,
who have re - fused; O sin - ner, hast - en, let Je - sus in,
Je - sus is true; All who be - lieve are safe from the storm,

CHORUS

Yes, He will pass, will pass o - ver you. When I see the
Then He will pass, will pass o - ver you.
Then God will pass, will pass o - ver you.
O He will pass, will pass o - ver you.

When I

blood, When I see the blood, When I see the
see the blood, When I see the blood, When I

blood, I will pass, I will pass, o - ver you.
see the blood, o - ver you.

No. 50 Ye Are The Light Of The World

Pearl Hatchett, arr. by E. S. D.

Emmett S. Dean

1. Oh, chris-tian, do not hide your light! For ye are the light of the world, But keep it trimmed and burn-ing bright, For ye are the light of the world. For ye are the light of the world, For ye are the light of the world; Then keep your lamps all burn-ing bright, For ye are the light of the world.

2. Go show to all the path of right, For ye are the light of the world, Go bring the stray-ing back to light, For ye are the light of the world.

3. Oh, do not let your light burn low, For ye are the light of the world, But keep it bright and on-ward go, For ye are the light, the light of the world, For ye are the light, the light of the world;

CHORUS

No. 51   Where The Soul Never Dies

W. M. G.

Wm. M. Golden

1. To Ca-naan's land I'm on my way, Where the soul (of man) nev-er dies;
2. A rose is bloom-ing there for me, Where the soul (of man) nev-er dies,
3. A love-light beams a-cross the foam, Where the soul (of man) nev-er dies,
4. My life will end in death-less sleep, Where the soul (of man) nev-er dies,
5. I'm on my way to that fair land, Where the soul (of man) nev-er dies;

My dark-est night will turn to-day, Where the soul (of man) nev-er dies.
And I will spend e-ter-ni-ty, Where the soul (of man) nev-er dies.
It shines to light the shores of home, Where the soul (of man) nev-er dies.
And ev-er-last-ing joys I'll reap, Where the soul (of man) nev-er dies.
Where there will be no part-ing hand, And the soul (of man) nev-er dies.

Chorus

No sad fare-wells, No tear - - dimmed eyes,
Dear friends, there'll be no sad fare-wells, There'll be no tear-dimmed eyes,

Where all is love, And the soul nev-er dies.
Where all is peace and joy and love, And the soul of man nev-er dies.

No. 52   Springtime In Glory

L. G. P.

Luther G. Presley

1. There is a hap-py land of sun-shine, I know, Free from all sor-row
2. Youth-ful and hap-py, none will ev - er grow old, Out in that love - ly
3. There is no weep-ing in that home of the soul, No death to bring to

pain and care; (from pain and care, the bless-ed) Land where no chill-ing winds of
land so fair; (so bright and fair, the land where) There is no suf - fer - ing from
us de-spair; (to bring de-spair, the land where) All will be glo - ry while the

death ev - er blow, Spring-time for-ev - er there.
hun - ger or cold,
a - ges shall roll, It is   O yes, 'tis al-ways spring-time.

CHORUS

Spring-time in glo - ry, (al-ways) spring-time in glo - ry, (Where the) flow - ers are

bloom-ing rich and rare;   An-gels are sing-ing
so rich and rare; Where hap - py   bells of

Springtime In Glory

glo - ry is ring-ing, It is Spring-time for-ev - er there. 'tis al-ways spring-time

No. 53   I Want To Go To Glory

Johnson Oatman, Jr.   H. M. Eagle

1. When I am thro' with toil and care, I want to go to glo - ry some day;
2. Tho' I a pil - grim now may roam, I want to go to glo - ry some day;
3. When I shall leave life's wea - ry road, I want to go to glo - ry some day;
4. No tears up there will dim the eye, I want to go to glo - ry some day;
5. Be - cause my Sav - ior lives on high, I want to go to glo - ry some day;

That land a - bove so bright and fair, I want to go to glo - ry some day.
This earth I know is not my home, I want to go to glo - ry some day.
When I at last lay down my load, I want to go to glo - ry some day.
There friends will nev - er say "good - by," I want to go to glo - ry some day.
To help to crown Him by and by, I want to go to glo - ry some day.

CHORUS

I want to go to glo - ry some day, (I do) My bless-ed Lord has promised I may;

That home so fair that waits just o - ver there, I want to go to glo - ry some day.

No. 54 — I'll Fly Away

A. E. B.   Albert E. Brumley

1. Some glad morn-ing when this life is o'er, I'll fly a-
2. When the shad-ows of this life have grown,
3. Just a few more wea-ry days and then, fly a-way

way; To a home on God's ce-les-tial shore,
fly a-way; Like a bird from pris-on bars has flown,
To a land where joys shall nev-er end,

CHORUS

I'll fly a-way. I'll fly a-
fly a-way, fly a-way. fly a-way,

way, O glo-ry, I'll fly a-way; When I die,
fly a-way, in the morn-ing,

Hal-le-lu-jah, by and by, I'll fly a-way.
fly a-way, fly a-way.

No. 55

What A Savior

Copyright, 1948, by The Stamps Quartet Music Co., Inc.
in "Guiding Hand"

M. P. D.

Marvin P. Dalton

Legato

1. Once I was stray-ing in sin's dark val-ley, No hope with-in could I
2. He left the Fa-ther, with all His rich-es, With calm-ness sweet and se-
3. Death's chill-y wa-ters I'll soon be cross-ing, His hand will lead me safe

see; They searched thru heav-en and found a Sav-ior To save a
rene, Came down from heav-en and gave His life-blood, To make the
o'er; I'll join the cho-rus in that great cit-y, And sing up

CHORUS

poor lost soul like me.
vil-est sin-ner clean. O what a Sav-ior, O hal-le-
there for-ev-er-more.

lu-jah, His heart was bro-ken on Cal-va-ry; His hands were

nail-scarred, His side was riv-en, He gave His life-blood for e-ven me.

No. 56 He Whispers Sweet Peace To Me

W. M. R.

Will M. Ramsey

1. Some-time when mis-giv-ings dark - en the day, and faith's light I
2. I could not go on with-out Him I know, The world would o'er-
3. I trust Him thru faith, by faith hold His hand, And some-times my
4. He speaks in a still, small voice we are told, A voice that dis-

can - not see; I ask my dear Lord to bright-en the way, He
whelm my soul; For I could not see the right way to go, When
faith is weak; And then when I ask Him to take com-mand, It
pels all fear; And when I'm in doubt, or trou - bled in soul, That

CHORUS

whis - pers sweet peace to me. Yes, He
temp - ta - tions o'er me roll.
seems that I hear Him speak.
still small voice I can hear. He whis - pers sweet peace to

whis-pers to me, He whis-pers sweet peace to me, When
me, ... He whis-pers sweet peace to me, ...

I am cast down in spir - it and soul, He whis-pers sweet peace to me.

Glory Enough for Me.

W. M. R.

Will M. Ramsey.

1. If the Sav-ior, at His com-ing, Finds me read-y— His blood my plea;
2. If I do His blest commandments Faithful un-til His face I see,—
3. O if I but do His bid-ding, Je-sus, who died to set me free,—
4. And when He shall come in glo-ry, Call-ing His own on land and sea,

With my lamp all trimmed and burning, 'Twill be glo-ry e-nough for me.
Just to see Him smile ap-prov-al Will be glo-ry e-nough for me.
Live each day as He would have me, There'll be glo-ry e-nough for me.
If with joy my soul can greet Him, 'Twill be glo-ry e-nough for me.

CHORUS.

Glo-ry e-nough for me, Glo-ry e-nough for me,
for me, for me,

If His com-ing finds me faith-ful, 'Twill be glo-ry e-nough for me.

No. 58   A New Name In Glory

1. I was once a sin-ner, but I came Par-don to receive from my Lord,
2. I was humbly kneeling at the cross, Fearing naught but God's angry frown,
3. In the book 'tis written, "Saved by grace;" O the joy that came to my soul!

This was free-ly giv-en, and I found That He always kept His word.
When the heavens opened and I saw That my name was written down.
Now I am for-giv-en, and I know, By the blood I am made whole.

kept His word.

Chorus

There's a new name written down in glory, And it's mine,   O yes, it's mine!
And it's mine,   yes, it's mine!

And the white-robed angels sing the story, "A sin-ner has come home;"
has come home;

For there's a new name written down in glo-ry, And it's mine,   O yes, it's
And it's mine,

A New Name In Glory

mine! With my sins for-giv-en I am bound for heaven, Nevermore to roam.
yes, it's mine!

No. 59   I Feel Like Traveling On

WM. HUNTER, D. D.   JAMES D. VAUGHAN.

1. My heav-'nly home   is bright and fair, I   feel like trav-el-ing   on;
2. Its   glit-t'ring tow'rs the sun out-shine, I   feel like trav-el-ing   on;
3. Let oth-ers seek   a home be-low, I   feel like trav-el-ing   on;
4. The Lord has been   so good to me, I   feel like trav-el-ing   on;

Nor pain, nor death   can en-ter there, I   feel like trav-el-ing   on.
That heav'nly man-sion shall be mine, I   feel like trav-el-ing   on.
Which flames de-vour, or waves o'er-flow, I   feel like trav-el-ing   on.
Un-til that bless-ed home I see, I   feel like trav-el-ing   on.

CHORUS.

Yes, I   feel like trav-el-ing   on,   I feel like trav-el-ing
     trav-el-ing on,

on;   My heav'nly home is bright and fair, I feel like trav-el-ing on.
trav-el-ing on;

No. 60   A Soul Winner For Jesus

"The law of the Lord is perfect, converting the soul."—Ps. 19:7.

J. W. F.   Copyright, Renewal, 1935, by Quartet Music Co.   J. W. Ferrill

1. I want to be a soul win-ner for Je-sus ev-'ry day, He does so much for me;
2. I want to be a soul win-ner and bring the lost to Christ, That they His grace may know;
3. I want to be a soul win-ner till Je-sus calls for me, To lay my bur-dens down;

I want to aid the lost sin-ner to leave his err-ing way, And be from bond-age free.
I want to live for Christ ev-er, and do His blessed will, Be-cause He loves me so.
I want to hear Him say, ser-vant, "You've gath-ered man-y sheaves, Re-ceive a star-ry crown."

CHORUS

A soul .... win-ner for Je - sus, A soul .... win-ner for
win-ner for Je-sus   Christ the Lord,   win-ner for Je-sus

Je - sus, O let me be each day; A soul .... win-ner for
Christ the Lord,   win-ner for Je-sus

Je - sus, A soul .... win-ner for Je - sus, He's done so much for me.
Christ the Lord,   win-ner for Je-sus   Christ the Lord,

No. 61 In The Shadow Of The Cross

Bernice M. Brostrom   W. H. Daniel

1. As we jour-ney on t'ward heaven's shin-ing goal, We may suf-fer
2. On that tree of sor-row Je-sus died for all, Took up-on Him-
3. There are souls to res-cue, there are souls to save, On the sea of

pain and loss; Burdens on-ly bring us blessings if we live
self our dross; As I see Him there I long to ev-er live
life they toss; May we be a light and teach them how to live

CHORUS

In the shad-ow of the cross. Are you liv-ing in the
shad-ow of the cross, Where the Savior took your place?
By the cross He'll lead us to that home above, There we'll see Him face to face.

No. 62 I Love To Tell The Story

Catherine Hankey

William G. Fischer

1. I love to tell the sto - ry Of un - seen things a - bove, Of
2. I love to tell the sto - ry, More won - der - ful it seems Than
3. I love to tell the sto - ry, 'Tis pleas - ant to re - peat What
4. I love to tell the sto - ry, For those who know it best Seem

Je - sus and His glo - ry, Of Je - sus and His love. I love to
all the gold - en fan - cies Of all our gold - en dreams. I love to
seems, each time I tell it, More won - der - ful - ly sweet. I love to
hun - ger - ing and thirst - ing To hear it like the rest. And when, in

tell the sto - ry, Be - cause I know 'tis true; It sat - is - fies my
tell the sto - ry, It did so much for me; And that is just the
tell the sto - ry, For some have nev - er heard The mes - sage of sal -
scenes of glo - ry, I sing the new, new song, 'Twill be the old, old

CHORUS

long - ings As noth - ing else can do.
rea - son I tell it now to thee. I love to tell the sto - ry, 'Twill
va - tion From God's own ho - ly Word.
sto - ry That I have loved so long.

be my theme in glo - ry To tell the old, old sto - ry Of Je - sus and His love.

No. 63 This World Is Not My Home

Arr.   J. R. Baxter, Jr.

1. This world is not my home, I'm just a pass-ing thru, My trea-sures
2. My Sav-ior par-doned me from guilt and shame I know, I'll trust His
3. I have a pre-cious moth-er up in glo-ry land, I don't ex-
4. The saints in glo-ry land are shout-ing vic-to-ry, I want to

are laid up some-where be-yond the blue; The an-gels beck-on me from
sav-ing grace while trav-'ling here be-low; I know He'll wel-come me at
pect to stop un-til I clasp her hand; For me she's wait-ing now at
join their band and live e-ter-nal-ly; I hear the sweet-est praise from

:S: FINE

heav-en's o-pen door, And I can't feel at home in this world an-y more.

CHORUS

O Lord, I know, I have no friend like you, If heav-en's not my home O

D.S.

Lord what can I do? The an-gels beck-on me from heav-en's o-pen door,

No. 64 Just Over In The Glory-Land

James W. Acuff   Emmett S. Dean

1. I've a home pre-pared where the saints a-bide, Just o - ver in the
2. I am on my way to those man-sions fair, Just o - ver in the
3. What a joy - ful tho't, that my Lord I'll see, Just o - ver in the
4. With the blood-washed throng I will shout and sing, Just o - ver in the

glo - ry-land; And I long to be by my Sav-ior's side, Just
glo - ry-land; There to sing God's praise, and His glo - ry share, Just
glo - ry-land; And with kin-dred saved, there for - ev - er be, Just
glo - ry-land; Glad ho - san - nas to Christ, the Lord and King, Just

CHORUS

o - ver in the glo - ry-land. Just o - ver in the glo - ry-land,
o - ver, o - ver

I'll join the hap - py an - gel band, Just o - ver in the
yes, join

glo - ry-land; Just o - ver in the glo - ry-land, There
o - ver, o - ver

Just Over In The Glory-Land

with the might-y host I'll stand, Just o - ver in the glo-ry-land.
yes, with

No. 65 Hold To God's Unchanging Hand

Jennie Wilson

F. L. Eiland
and Clyde Williams

1. Time is filled with swift tran-si-tion, Naught of earth unmoved can stand,
2. Trust in Him who will not leave you, What-so - ev - er years may bring,
3. Cov - et not this world's vain rich-es, That so rap-id - ly de - cay,
4. When your journey is com-plet-ed, If to God you have been true,

Rit.

Build your hopes on things e - ter - nal, Hold to God's unchanging hand!
If by earth-ly friends for - sak - en, Still more close-ly to Him cling!
Seek to gain the heav'n-ly treasures, They will nev - er pass a - way!
Fair and bright the home in glo - ry, Your en - rap-tured soul will view!

CHORUS

Hold to God's un-chang-ing hand! Hold to God's unchanging hand!
to His hand, to His hand,

Rit.

Build your hopes on things e - ter - nal, Hold to God's un-chang-ing hand!

No. 66 I've Never Loved Him Better

James Rowe

W. B. Walbert

1. Since Je-sus came and found me, and put His arms a-round me, And all my
2. Al-though I have been clinging to Him and sweet-ly sing-ing, And He has
3. Oh, bless-ed Friend su-per-nal, my hope and joy e-ter-nal! Keep Thou my

gall-ing fet-ters took a-way; Al-though I've loved Him dear-ly, and
been my com-fort and my stay; And I have told His sto-ry, and
soul till shad-ows flee a-way; For night-ly I would say, Lord, till

trust-ed Him sin-cere-ly, I've nev-er loved Him bet-ter than to-day.
la-bored for His glo-ry, I've nev-er loved Him bet-ter than to-day.
end the pil-grim way, Lord, "I've nev-er loved Him bet-ter than to-day."

Chorus

I've nev-er loved Him bet-ter than to-day, ... I've nev-er
loved Him bet-ter than to-day,

felt Him clos-er on the way; .... And, oh, how sweet the feel-ing,
felt Him clos-er on the way;

I've Never Loved Him Better

rit

When in His presence kneel-ing, I've nev-er loved Him bet-ter than to-day.

No. 67 Blessed Be The Name

Charles Wesley

R. E. Hudson

1. O for a thousand tongues to sing, Bless-ed be the name of the Lord!
2. Je - sus! the name that charms our fears, Bless-ed be the name of the Lord!
3. He breaks the pow'r of can - celed sin, Bless-ed be the name of the Lord!
4. I nev - er shall for-get that day, Bless-ed be the name of the Lord!

The glo - ries of my God and King! Bless-ed be the name of the Lord!
'Tis mu - sic in the sin - ner's ears, Bless-ed be the name of the Lord!
His blood can make the foul - est clean, Bless-ed be the name of the Lord!
When Je - sus washed my sins a - way, Bless-ed be the name of the Lord!

CHORUS

Bless-ed be the name, bless-ed be the name, Bless-ed be the name of the Lord!

Bless-ed be the name, bless-ed be the name, Bless-ed be the name of the Lord!

No. 68

Victory

B. E. W.

B. E. Warren

1. Hal - le - lu - jah, what a thought! Je - sus full sal - va - tion brought,
2. I am trust - ing in the Lord, I am stand - ing on His word,
3. Shout your free - dom ev - 'ry - where, His e - ter - nal peace de - clare,
4. We will sing it on that shore, When this fleet - ing life is o'er,

Vic - to - ry, vic - to - ry. Let the pow'rs of sin as - sail,
Vic - to - ry, vic - to - ry. I have peace and joy with - in,
Vic - to - ry, vic - to - ry. Let us sing it here be - low,
Vic - to - ry, vic - to - ry. Sing it here, ye ran - somed throng,

Vic - to - ry, vic - to - ry.

Heav - en's grace can nev - er fail, Vic - to - ry, vic - to - ry.
Since my life is free from sin, Vic - to - ry, vic - to - ry.
In the face of ev - 'ry foe, Vic - to - ry, vic - to - ry.
Start the ev - er - last - ing song:- Vic - to - ry, vic - to - ry.

Vic - to - ry, vic - to - ry.

CHORUS

Vic - to - ry .... yes, vic - to - ry; Hal - le - lu - jah! I am

Vic - to - ry, yes, vic - to - ry;

free, Je - sus gives me vic - to - ry; Glo - ry, glo - ry, hal - le -

Glo - ry, glo - ry,

Owned by R. E. Winsett, Dayton, Tenn.

Victory

lu - jah! He is all............in all to me............
hal - le - lu - jah! He is all, He is all in all to me. (all to me.)

No. 69 More About Jesus

E. E. Hewitt

Jno. R. Sweney

1. More a-bout Je-sus would I know, More of His grace to oth-ers show;
2. More a-bout Je-sus let me learn, More of His ho - ly will dis-cern;
3. More a-bout Je-sus in His word, Hold-ing com-mun-ion with my Lord;
4. More a-bout Je-sus on His throne, Rich-es in glo - ry all His own;

More of His sav-ing full-ness see, More of His love who died for me.
Spir-it of God my teach-er be, Show-ing the things of Christ to me.
Hear-ing His voice in ev - 'ry line, Mak-ing each faith-ful say-ing mine.
More of His king-dom's sure in-crease, More of His com-ing, Prince of Peace.

CHORUS

More, more a-bout Je - sus, More, more a - bout Je - sus;

More of His sav-ing full-ness see, More of His love who died for me.

Beautiful

B. E. Warren

1. Beau - ti - ful robes so white, Beau-ti - ful land of light, Beau-ti - ful
2. Beau - ti - ful tho't to me, We shall for - ev - er be Thine in e -
3. Beau - ti - ful things on high, O - ver in yon - der sky, Thus I shall

home so bright, Where there shall come no night; Beau-ti-ful crown I'll wear,
ter - ni - ty, When from this world we're free; Free from its toil and care,
leave this shore, Counting my treas-ures o'er; Where we shall nev - er die,

Shining with stars o'er there, Yonder in mansions fair, Gather us there.
Heav-en - ly joys to share, Let me cross o-ver there; This is my pray'r.
Car - ry me by and by, Nev-er to sor-row more, Heav-en-ly store.

Chorus

Beau-ti - ful robes,............ ....Beau - ti - ful land,...............
Beau-ti - ful robes of white,   Beau-ti - ful land of light,

Beau-ti - iul home,................ Beau-tl - ful band,...............
Beau-ti - ful home so bright,   Beau-ti - ful band of might,

Beautiful

Beau-ti-ful crown, Shining so fair,
Beau-ti-ful, beau-ti-ful crown, Shining, yes, shining so fair,

Beau-ti-ful man - sion bright, Gather us there.
Beautiful mansion bright, yes, gather us there.

No. 71   I Would Not Be Denied

C. P. J.   C. P. Jones

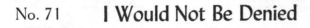

1. When pangs of death seized on my soul; Un-to the Lord I cried, Till Jesus came and
2. As Ja-cob in the days of old, I wrestled with the Lord; And instant, with a
3. Old Satan said my Lord was gone And would not hear my pray'r, But praise the Lord! the

CHORUS

made me whole, I would not be de-nied. I would not be de-nied, I would not
cour - age bold, I stood up - on His word.
work is done, And Christ the Lord is here.   de-nied,

be de-nied, Till Jesus came and made me whole, I would not be de-nied.
de-nied,   de-nied.

No.72 It Won't Be Very Long

Rev. Morgan Williams   E. M. Bartlett

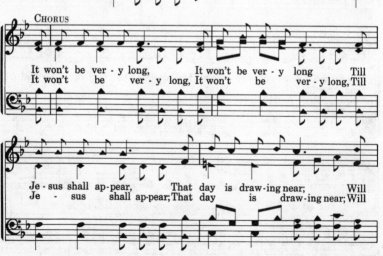

1. It won't be ver - y long till this short life shall end, It won't be ver - y
2. It won't be ver - y long till here we cease to roam, It won't be ver - y
3. It won't be ver - y long till bur - dens we lay down, It won't be ver - y
4. It won't be ver - y long till earth shall pass a - way, It won't be ver - y

long till Je - sus shall de - scend; And then the dead in Christ from
long till all the saints get home; And then with smil - ing face we'll
long till we'll re - ceive a crown; And then we'll shout and sing with
long till works of men de - cay; But Je - sus has pre - pared a

beds of clay shall rise To meet the Lord and King up yon - der in the skies.
walk the street of gold, And sing the Sav - ior's praise where saints are nev - er old.
an - gels round the throne, And when we meet up there, we'll know as we are known.
hap - py dwell - ing place, For all who look a - bove and trust His match - less grace.

CHORUS

It won't be ver - y long,   It won't be ver - y long   Till
It won't be ver - y long, It won't be ver - y long, Till

Je - sus shall ap - pear,   That day is draw - ing near;   Will
Je - sus shall ap - pear; That day is draw - ing near; Will

No. 74 He Bore It All

J. R. Baxter, Jr.   Virgil O. Stamps

1. My pre-cious Sav-ior suf-fered pain and ag-o-ny, He bore it
2. They placed a crown of thorns up-on my Sav-ior's head,
3. Up Cal-v'ry's hill in shame the bless-ed Sav-ior trod,

all   that I might live;   He broke the bonds of
                                               By cru-el man with
Free-ly bore it all   I with Him might live; Between two thieves they

sin and set the cap-tive free,   All   that   I   might
spear His side was pierced and bled,
cru-ci-fied the Son of God, He bore it all   that   I   might

FINE CHORUS

in His presence live. He bore it   all   that   I might see His
live.   Je-sus bore it all,

shin-ing face,   Free-ly bore it all,
see His shin-ing face, He bore it all,   that I might

He Bore It All

I with Him might live; I stood condemned to die but Jesus took my place,
live; Stood condemned to die, freely took my place,

D.S.

No. 75

Old Time Power

"They were all filled with the Holy Ghost."--Acts 2:4.

C. D. T.   Charles D. Tillman

1. They were in an up-per chamber, They were all with one ac-cord,
2. Yes, this pow'r from heav'n descended With the sound of rush-ing wind;
3. Yes, this "old time" pow'r was giv-en To our fa-thers who were true;

When the Ho-ly Ghost de-scend-ed, As was prom-ised by our Lord.
Tongues of fire came down up-on them, As the Lord said He would send.
This is prom-ised to be-liev-ers, And we all may have it, too.

CHORUS

O Lord, send the pow'r just now; O Lord, send the pow'r just now;

O Lord, send the pow'r just now, And bap-tize ev-'ry one.

No. 76   It's Really Surprising
(What The Lord Can Do)

Copyright, 1948, by The Hartford Music & Printing Co., Inc.
in "Grace and Glory"

A. E. B.

Albert E. Brumley

1. If you are bur-dened down with care, Take it to Je-sus Christ in prayer,
2. When you are lost and can-not see, Je-sus will hear your fee-ble plea,
3. If you are wand'ring from the fold He can re-deem your pre-cious soul,

Real-ly sur-pris-ing What the Lord can do;
It's real-ly sur-pris-ing What the Lord can do;

He can give glad-ness day and night, He can change dark-ness in-to light,
Bless-ings He gives to one and all Who on His pre-cious name will call,
Je-sus will be your dear-est friend, He will go with you till the end,

FINE

Real-ly sur-pris-ing what the Lord can do.
It's real-ly surprising What the Lord can do.

CHORUS

Real-ly sur-pris-ing What the Lord can do,
It's real-ly sur-pris-ing What the Lord can do,

It's Really Surprising
(What The Lord Can Do)

Make a lost sin-ner Just as good as new;
He can make a lost sin-ner Just as good as new;

D.S.

If you will let Him He will par-don you,
And if you will let Him He'll par-don you,

No. 77 Blessed Jesus Loves You Too

A. E. B.   Albert E. Brumley

1. On the rug-ged cross of Cal-va-ry Je-sus gave His life for you,
2. When the burdens press on ev-'ry hand, When you know not what to do;
3. Come and seek His pre-cious, ten-der care, He will save and par-don you;

FINE

Tho the vil-est sin-ner you may be,
Just re-mem-ber Christ will un-der-stand, Bless-ed Je-sus loves you too.
Ev-'ry sor-row He will glad-ly bear,

D.S.-Tho the vil-est sin-ner you may be,

CHORUS   D.S.

Bless-ed Je-sus dear-ly loves you, He's a friend so kind and true;

I Know Who Holds Tomorrow

(But I know who holds my hand.)

Words and Music by Ira Stanphill

1. I don't know   a-bout to-mor-row,   I just live from
2. Ev-'ry step   is get-ting bright-er,   As the gold - en
3. I don't know   a-bout to-mor-row,   It may bring   me

day to day;   I don't bor - row from its sun-shine,   For its
stairs I climb;   Ev - 'ry bur - den's get-ting light-er,   Ev-'ry
pov - er - ty;   But the one   who feeds the spar-row,   Is the

skies   may turn to gray;   I don't wor - ry o'er the fu -ture,
cloud   is sil-ver lined; There the sun   is al-ways shin-ing,
one   who stands by me;   And the path   that be my por-tion,

For   I know   what Je - sus said;   And to-day   I'll walk be-
There no tear   will dim the eye;   At the end - ing of the
May   be through the flame or flood;   But His pres - ence goes be-

CHORUS

side Him,   For He knows   what is a - head.
rain-bow, Where the moun-tains touch the sky.   Man - y things a-
fore me,   And I'm cov - ered with His blood.

I Know Who Holds Tomorrow

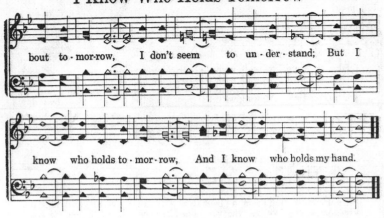

bout to - mor-row, I don't seem to un - der - stand; But I

know who holds to - mor - row, And I know who holds my hand.

No. 79   Not Made With Hands

Arr.   Old Melody Arr.

1. Christ went a build-ing to pre-pare, Not made with hands; And 'twill be decked with
2. Put on the ar - mor of our God, Not made with hands; And take the path our
3. With shield of faith de - fy the foe; Not made with hands; Un - til you hear the
4. Then come up, children, get your crown, Not made with hands; When you have laid your

FINE CHORUS

jew - els rare, Not made with hands.
Cap - tain trod, Not made with hands. I know (I know,) I know (I know,)
trum-pet blow, Not made with hands.
ar - mor down, Not made with hands.

D. S.

I have an - oth - er build-ing; I know (I know,) I know (I know.)

No. 80 I Love To Walk With Jesus

C. F. W.

C. F. Weigele

1. Oh, I love to walk with Je-sus Like the pub-li-cans of old,
2. Oh, I love to walk with Je-sus Like the man of long a-go,
3. Oh, I love to walk with Je-sus All the way to Cal-v'ry's brow,
4. Oh, some-time I'll walk with Je-sus In the land of end-less day,

When He gath-ered them a-bout Him And the bless-ed tid-ings told;
Who had tar-ried by the way-side Near the gates of Jer-i-cho;
Gaze up-on that scene of suf-f'ring, While my tears of sor-row flow;
When our jour-ney here is o-ver And we've reached our home to stay;

How He came to bring de-liv-'rance To the cap-tives in dis-tress,
Je-sus heard his cry for mer-cy, Gave him back his sight that day,
There He tells me how He loves me, Takes my ev-'ry sin a-way,
Then I'll walk with Him for-ev-er, Sing His prais-es o'er and o'er,

Take a-way our ev-'ry bur-den, Giv-ing per-fect peace and rest.
And im-me-diate-ly he fol-lowed Je-sus all a-long the way.
So I fol-low Him so glad-ly, Lead me an-y-where He may.
Laugh and shout, and ev-er tell Him That I love Him more and more.

CHORUS

I will fol-low where He lead-eth, I will pas-ture where He feed-eth,

I Love To Walk With Jesus

I will fol-low all the way, Lord, I will fol-low Je-sus ev-'ry day.

No. 81 He's Coming Again

F. L. E. Copyright, 1906, by F. L. Eiland F. L. Eiland

1. Oh, would you be num-bered as one of His fold? Be spot-less with-
2. Not known is the mo-ment when He shall ap-pear, To gath-er them
3. The voice of His Spir-it says, Read-y then be; Oh, will you be-
4. Risk not an ac-cept-ance of Him in that day, All cov-ered with

in; Be watch-ing and wait-ing that sight to be-hold;
in; The souls who have fol-lowed Him faith-ful-ly here; He's com-ing a-
gin? If peace in His pres-ence you hope to then see;
sin; Be robed and all read-y, the Spir-it doth say;

CHORUS

gain. He's com-ing a-gain, (a-gain)! He's com-ing a-gain, (a-gain)!

Be watch-ing and wait-ing that sight to be-hold; He's com-ing a-gain.

No. 82 — I'll Have A New Life

L. G. P.

Luther G. Presley

1. On the res-ur-rec-tion morn-ing when all the dead in Christ shall rise,
2. Free from ev-'ry im-per-fec-tion, youth-ful and hap-py I shall be,
3. What a hal-le-lu-jah morn-ing when the last trump of God shall sound,

I'll have a new bod-y, Praise the Lord, I'll have a new life; e-ter-nal;

Sown in weak-ness, raised in pow-er, read-y to live in Par-a-dise,
Glo-ri-fied with Him for-ev-er, death will be lost in vic-to-ry,
Graves all burst-ing, saints a shout-ing, heav-en-ly beau-ty all a-round,

I'll have a new bod-y, Praise the Lord I'll have a new life. O yes.

CHORUS

Glo-ry, glo-ry, nev-er sad,
I'll have a new home of love e-ter-nal with the re-deemed of God to stand,

I'll Have A New Life

There'll be no more sor-row, No more pain, there'll be no more strife; no strife;

Yes, raised in the like-ness of my Sav-ior, read-y to live in glo-ry land, In His like-ness, I'll be glad,

I'll have a new bod-y, Praise the Lord, I'll have a new life. e-ter-nal.

No. 83   He Knows

G. W. Lyon

1. He knows the bit-ter, wea-ry way, The end-less striv-ings day by day,
2. He knows how hard the fight has been, The clouds that come our lives between,
3. He knows when faint and worn we sink, How deep the pain, how near the brink
4. He knows, O tho't so full of bliss! For tho on earth our joys we miss,

The souls that weep, the souls that pray, He knows, He knows.
The wounds the world has nev-er seen,
Of dark de-spair, we pause and shrink,
We still can bear it feel-ing this, He knows, He knows.

No. 84 Just A Little Talk With Jesus

Spiritual

Cleavant Derricks

1. I once was lost in sin but Je-sus took me in, And then a lit-tle
2. Some-times my path seems drear, with-out a ray of cheer, And then a cloud of
3. I may have doubts and fears, my eyes be filled with tears, But Je-sus is a

light from heav-en filled my soul; It bathed my heart in love and wrote my
doubt may hide the light of day; The mists of sin may rise and hide the
friend who watch-es day and night; I go to Him in pray'r, He knows my

name a-bove, And just a lit-tle talk with Je-sus made me whole.....
star-ry skies, But just a lit-tle talk with Je-sus clears the way.....
ev-'ry care, And just a lit-tle talk with Je-sus makes it right.....

CHORUS

Have a lit-tle talk with Je-sus   tell Him all a-bout our
Now let us   let us

trou-bles,   Hear our faint-est cry   an-swer by and by;
He will   and He will

Just A Little Talk With Jesus

Now when you Feel a lit-tle pray'r wheel turn-ing, and you know a lit-tle fire is

burn-ing, You will Find a lit-tle talk with Je-sus makes it right.......... it makes it right.

No. 85 Have Thine Own Way, Lord

Copyright 1907. Renewal 1935 by G. C. Stebbins.
Assigned to Hope Pub. Co. Used by per.

Adelaide A. Pollard

Geo. C. Stebbins

1. Have Thine own way, Lord! Have Thine own way! Thou art the
2. Have Thine own way, Lord! Have Thine own way! Search me and
3. Have Thine own way, Lord! Have Thine own way! Wound-ed and
4. Have Thine own way, Lord! Have Thine own way! Hold o'er my

Pot-ter, I am the clay. Mould me and make me
try me, Mas-ter, to-day! Whit-er than snow, Lord,
wea-ry, Help me, I pray! Pow-er, all pow-er,
be-ing, Ab-so-lute sway! Fill with Thy Spir-it

Aft-er Thy will, While I am wait-ing, Yield-ed and still.
Wash me just now, As in Thy pres-ence Hum-bly I bow.
Sure-ly is Thine! Touch me and heal me, Sav-ior di-vine!
Till all shall see Christ on-ly, al-ways, Liv-ing in me!

No. 86 Keep On The Firing Line

J. R. Baxter, Jr.

1. If you're in the bat-tle for the Lord and right,
2. God will on-ly use a sol-dier He can trust,
3. When we get to heav-en we shall be so glad,

Keep on the fir-ing line, If you win the vict'-ry, broth-er, you must fight,
Keep on the fir-ing line, If you wear the crown, then bear the cross you must,
fir-ing line, We shall praise the Sav-ior for the call we had,

Keep on the fir-ing line; There are man-y dan-gers which we all must face,
Life is but to la-bor for the Mas-ter dear,
my brother; 'Twill be joy to see the souls we helped to win,

If we die still fight-ing it is no dis-grace,
Help to ban-ish dark-ness and to spread good cheer,
Those we led to Je-sus, from the paths of sin,

Cow-ards in the service should not have a place, Keep on the fir-ing line.
We shall be re-warded for our ser-vice here,
Hear their welcome plau-dit and go march-ing in, fir-ing line.

Keep On The Firing Line

Chorus

You must fight and be brave against all e-vil, Nev-er run, tho foes combine;

If you would fight for God and right, Keep on the fir-ing line.

fir-ing line.

No. 87   Follow On

Mrs. E. Greer Floyd   Adapted by F. L. E.   Jas. B. Franklin

1. My soul o'erflows with joy and peace, Where Je-sus shows His face, And bids all
2. Thro' shadows deep, He lights the way, And leads my soul a-long To man-sions
3. When to death's narrow stream I come, Tho' dark the wave and cold, My Lord doth
4. All glo-ry to His pre-cious name, Who gave His life for me; His grace, His

FINE   CHORUS

doubt and sorrows cease, And saves me by His grace! O will you fol-low on?
fair and end-less day, The land of praise and song.
call my spir-it home In-to His peace-ful fold.
good-ness, I'll pro-claim Thro' all e-ter-ni-ty. O will you fol-low, fol-low on?

D. S.—O will you fol-low on?

D. S.

O will you fol-low on?   O will you fol-low where He leads?
O will you fol-low, fol-low on?

Spiritual

Chas. E. Pace and J. R. Baxter, Jr.

C. E. P.

1. When my bur-dens seem so heav-y and my load is hard to bear,
2. When my heart is bowed in sor-row and my way is dark as night,
3. When the clouds hang low and heav-y and my body's racked with pain,

I'm gon-na cling, I'm gon-na cling; I'm gon-na cling, I'm gon-na cling;

He has prom-ised if I serve Him He will light-en ev-'ry care,
When old Sa-tan's arm-y march-ing tries to put my soul to flight,
Je-sus is my guide and Cap-tain and His sun-shine fol-lows rain,

I'm gon-na cling, I'm gon-na cling. I'm gon-na cling, I'm gon-na cling.

Chorus

I'm gonna cling to the cross till Jesus sets me free, I promised I would serve Him

I'm Gonna Cling to the Cross Till I Die

if He bro't the light to me; I'm gon-na cling, cling, I'm gon-na I'm gon-na

cling, I'm gon-na cling to the cross till I die.
I'm gon-na cling,.......... till I die.

No. 89 Take My Hand, Precious Lord

T. A. D.

Thomas A. Dorsey

1. When my way grow-eth drear, pre-cious Lord lin-ger near, When my life
2. When the shad-ows ap - pear, and the night draw-eth near, And the day

Chorus Pre-cious Lord, take my hand, lead me on, let me stand, I am tired,

is al - most gone; Hear my cry, hear my call, hold my hand
is past and gone; At the riv - er I stand, guide my feet,

I am weak, I am worn; Thru the storm, thru the night, lead me on

lest I fall; Take my hand, pre-cious Lord, lead me home.
hold my hand;

to the light; Take my hand, pre-cious Lord, lead me home.

90 I've Got That Old Time Religion in My Heart

H. M.   Hurdist Milsap

1. I'm glad Jesus came, glory to His name, O what a friend is He;
2. What a joy to know One who loves us so, He is so kind and true;
3. Sinner won't you now humbly to Him bow, Just let the Lord come in;

He so freely gave His own life to save, From bonds of sin set free.
He has changed my life from all sin and strife, He'll do the same for you.
You'll find perfect peace, joy will never cease, You shall the life-crown win.

Chorus

I've got that pure love in my heart,
I've got that old time religion in my heart, A

It is now way down inside, I've got that new peace
way down inside, I've got a new kind of feeling in my

in my heart, Where true joys will e'er abide; Nobody knows what it
heart, True joys abide;

I've Got That Old Time Religion in My Heart

means to me, No-bod-y knows but my Lord and me,

I've got that
I've got that old

pure love in my heart, It is now way down in-side.
time re-li-gion in my heart, A-way down in-side.

We'll Work Till Jesus Comes

No. 91

Elizabeth Mills

William Miller

1. O land of rest for, thee I sigh! When will the mo-ment come When
2. To Je-sus Christ I fled for rest! He bade me cease to roam, And
3. I sought at once my Sav-ior's side, No more my steps shall roam; With

Chorus

I shall lay my ar-mor by, And dwell in peace at home? We'll work till
lean for suc-cor on His breast Till He con-duct me home.
Him I'll brave death's chilling tide, And reach my heav'nly home. We'll work

1

2

Je-sus comes, We'll work till Je-sus comes;
We'll work

And we'll be gathered home.

No. 92   Victory In Jesus

E. M. B.   Eugene M. Bartlett

1. I heard an old, old sto - ry, How a Sav - ior came from glo - ry,
2. I heard a - bout His heal - ing, Of His cleans-ing pow'r re - veal - ing,
3. I heard a - bout a man - sion He has built for me in glo - ry,

How He gave His life on Cal - va - ry To save a wretch like me;
How He made the lame to walk a - gain And caused the blind to see;
And I heard a - bout the streets of gold Be - yond the crys - tal sea;

I heard a - bout His groan-ing, Of His pre-cious blood's a - ton - ing,
And then I cried "dear Je - sus, Come and heal my brok - en spir - it,"
A - bout the an - gels sing - ing, And the old re - demp-tion sto - ry,

Then I re - pent - ed of my sins And won the vic - to - ry.
And some - how Je - sus came and bro't To me the vic - to - ry.
And some sweet day I'll sing up there The song of vic - to - ry.

Chorus

O vic - to - ry in Je - sus, My Sav - ior, for - ev - er, He sought me and

Victory In Jesus

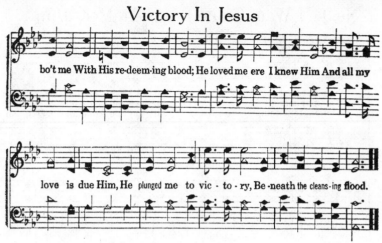

bo't me With His re-deem-ing blood; He loved me ere I knew Him And all my

love is due Him, He plunged me to vic - to - ry, Be -neath the cleans-ing flood.

© Copyright 1940. Renewal 1968 by Stamps-Baxter Music & Printing Co.
All Rights Reserved

No. 93   Hand In Hand With Jesus

Rev. Johnson Oatman, Jr.   L. D. Huffstutler

1. Once from my poor sin - sick soul Christ did ev - 'ry bur - den roll,
2. In my night of dark de - spair, Je - sus heard and answered pray'r,
3. From the straight and nar - row way, Praise the Lord, I can - not stray,
4. When the stars are back - ward rolled And His home I shall be - hold,

Fine

Now I walk re-deemed and whole,
Now I'm walk-ing free as air, Hand in hand with Je - sus.
For I'm walk-ing ev - 'ry day,
I will walk those streets of gold,

D.S.—Walk-ing thus, I can - not stray, Hand in hand with Je - sus.
Chorus   **D.S.**

Hand in hand we walk each day, Hand in hand a - long the way,

No. 94 I Want To Be Ready To Meet Him

Adger M. Pace   G. T. Speer

1. You may have your world-ly pleas-ures, your sil - ver and your gold, You may
2. You may talk a - bout your rich - es, your dia-monds and your pearls, You may
3. There is one thing I can boast of, sal - va - tion from the fall, I'm an

pile up all the rich - es that this old world can hold; But I'd rath - er
gain the wealth for a - ges of this and all the worlds, But the Sav-iour
heir to wealth in glo - ry, my Fa - ther owns it all; That is why I'm

D.S.- to meet Him in the sky; Oh, I want to

have my Sav - iour, and with Him firm - ly stand, For I want to be
is more pre - cious, with Him I'll take my stand, For I want to be
shout - ing hap - py and go at His com-mand, For I want to be

be more like Him, and do His blest com-mand, For I want to be

FINE   CHORUS

read - y to meet Him in the glo - ry land. I want to be
                                              I want to be

D.S.

read - y to meet Him by and by, I want to be read - y
read - y   I want to be   read - y

Jesus Is All I Need

James Rowe

Adger M. Pace

1. When I am bur-dened, or wea-ry and sad, Je-sus is all I need; Nev-er He fails to up-lift and make glad, Je-sus is all I need.

2. When I am tempt-ed and fear I may fall, Je-sus is all I need; He nev-er fails to re-spond to my call, Je-sus is all I need.

3. When I am swept by the tem-pests of life, Je-sus is all I need; Peace He im-parts, what-so-ev-er the strife, Je-sus is all I need.

4. When thro' the val-ley He calls me to go, Je-sus is all I'll need; He will be with me to cheer me, I know, Je-sus is all I'll need.

CHORUS

All that I need He will al-ways be, All that I need till His face I see; All that I need thro' e-ter-ni-ty, Je-sus is all I need.

No. 96 — Leave It There

C. Albert Tindley
Arr. Chas. A. Tindley, Jr.

Moderato

1. If the world from you with-hold of its sil-ver and its gold, And you
2. If your bod-y suf-fers pain and your health you can't re-gain, And your
3. When your en-e-mies as-sail and your heart be-gins to fail, Don't for-
4. When your youthful days are gone and old age is steal-ing on, And your

have to get a-long with meager fare, Just re-mem-ber, in His word, how He
soul is al-most sink-ing in de-spair, Je-sus knows the pain you feel, He can
get that God in heav-en answers pray'r; He will make a way for you and will
bod-y bends beneath the weight of care; He will nev-er leave you then, He'll go

feeds the lit-tle bird;
save and He can heal; Take your burden to the Lord and leave it there. Leave it
lead you safe-ly thru;
with you to the end;

Fine   Chorus

there,   leave it   there,   Take your burden to the Lord and leave it
Leave it there,   leave it   there,

there;   If you trust and nev-er doubt, He will sure-ly bring you out;
leave it there;

D.S.

Will Jesus Find Us Watching?

"Let us not sleep, as do others; but let us watch and be sober." —1 Thes. 5:6

Fanny J. Crosby   W. H. Doane

1. When Je - sus comes to re-ward His serv-ants, Wheth-er it be
2. If at the dawn of the ear - ly morn-ing, He shall call us
3. Have we been true to the trust He left us? Do we seek to
4. Bless - ed are those whom the Lord finds watching, In His glo - ry

noon or night, Faith - ful to Him will He find us watch-ing,
one by one, When to the Lord we re - store our tal - ents,
do our best! If in our hearts there is naught con-demns us,
they shall share; If He shall come at the dawn or mid-night,

CHORUS

With our lamps all trimmed and bright?
Will He an - swer thee, "Well done?" O can we say, we are read - y,
We shall have a glo - rious rest.
Will He find us watch-ing there?

broth - er? Read - y for the soul's bright home? Say will He find you and

me still watch-ing, Wait - ing, wait - ing when the Lord shall come?

No. 98 — Throw Out The Lifeline

Rev. Edward S. Ufford

E. S. U. Arr. by Geo. C. Stebbins

1. Throw out the Life-line a-cross the dark wave, There is a broth-er whom
2. Throw out the Life-line with hand quick and strong, Why do you tar-ry, why
3. Throw out the Life-line to dan-ger-fraught men, Sink-ing in an-guish where
4. Soon will the sea-son of res-cue be o'er, Soon will they drift to e-

some one should save; Some-bod-y's broth-er! O who then will dare To
lin-ger so long? See! he is sink-ing; O has-ten to-day—And
you've nev-er been: Winds of temp-ta-tion and bil-lows of woe Will
ter-ni-ty's shore, Hast then, my broth-er, no time for de-lay, But

CHORUS

throw out the Life-line, His per-il to share?
out with the Life-boat! a-way then a-way! Throw out the Life-line!
soon hurl them out where the dark wa-ters flow.
throw out the Life-line and save them to-day.

throw out the Life-line! Some one is drift-ing a-way; Throw out the

Life-line! throw out the Life-line! Some one is sink-ing to-day.

Trust And Obey

Rev. J. H. Sammis   D. B. Towner

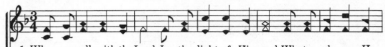

1. When we walk with the Lord In the light of His word, What a glo-ry He
2. Not a shad-ow can rise, Not a cloud in the skies, But His smile quick-ly
3. Not a bur-den we bear, Not a sor-row we share, But our toil He doth
4. But we nev-er can prove The de-lights of His love Un-til all on the
5. Then in fel-low-ship sweet We will sit at His feet, Or we'll walk by His

sheds on our way! While we do His good will, He a-bides with us
drives it a-way; Not a doubt nor a fear, Not a sigh nor a
rich-ly re-pay; Not a grief nor a loss, Not a frown nor a
al-tar we lay; For the fav-or He shows, And the joy He be-
side in the way; What He says we will do, Where He sends we will

CHORUS

still, And with all who will trust and o-bey.
tear Can a-bide while we trust and o-bey. Trust and o-bey, For there's
cross, But is blest if we trust and o-bey.
stows, Are for all who will trust and o-bey.
go, Nev-er fear, on-ly trust and o-bey.

no oth-er way To be hap-py in Je-sus But to trust and o-bey.

Tell It To Jesus

"Tell it to Jesus." Matt. 14:12

E. S. Lorenz

1. Are you wea-ry, are you heav-y heart-ed? Tell it to Je-sus,
2. Do the tears flow down your cheeks un-bid-den? Tell it to Je-sus,
3. Do you fear the gath-'ring clouds of sor-row? Tell it to Je-sus,
4. Are you trou-bled at the tho't of dy-ing? Tell it to Je-sus,

tell it to Je-sus, Are you griev-ing o-ver joys de-part-ed?
tell it to Je-sus, Have you sins that to man's eyes are hid-den?
tell it to Je-sus, Are you anx-ious what shall be to-mor-row?
tell it to Je-sus, For Christ's com-ing, dai-ly are you sigh-ing?

CHORUS

Tell it to Je-sus a-lone. Tell it to Je-sus, tell it to Je-sus, He is a friend that's well known; You have no oth-er such a friend or broth-er, Tell it to Je-sus a-lone.

No. 101 There Is Power In The Blood

L. E. J.

L. E. Jones

1. Would you be free from your bur-den of sin? There's pow'r in the blood,
2. Would you be free from your pas-sion and pride? There's pow'r in the blood,
3. Would you be whit-er, much whit-er than snow? There's pow'r in the blood,
4. Would you do ser-vice for Je-sus your King? There's pow'r in the blood,

pow'r in the blood; Would you o'er e-vil a vic-to-ry win?
pow'r in the blood; Come for a cleans-ing to Cal-va-ry's tide,
pow'r in the blood; Sin-stains are lost in its life-giv-ing flow,
pow'r in the blood; Would you live dai-ly, His prais-es to sing?

CHORUS

There's won-der-ful pow'r in the blood. There is pow'r, pow'r,
there is pow'r,

wonder-working pow'r In the blood of the Lamb; There is
In the blood of the Lamb;

pow'r, pow'r, wonder-working pow'r In the pre-cious blood of the Lamb.
there is pow'r,

No. 102 There's A Great Day Coming

W. L. T.

W. L. Thompson

1. There's a great day com-ing, a great day com-ing, There's a great day com-ing by and by, When the saints and the sin-ners shall be part - ed, right and left,

2. There's a bright day com-ing, a bright day com-ing, There's a bright day com-ing by and by, But its bright-ness shall on - ly come to them that love the Lord,

3. There's a sad day com-ing, a sad day com-ing, There's a sad day com-ing by and by, When the sin - ner shall hear his doom, "De-part, I know ye not,"

Are you read - y for that day to come?

Chorus

Are you read - y, are you read - y? Are you read - y for the judg-ment day? Are you read - y, are you read - y For the judg-ment day?

No. 103 Turned Away From The Beautiful Gate

D. E. Dortch

D. E. Dortch

Not too fast

1. Some-one will knock at the saints' bright home, And hear the Lord say-ing, "You
2. Some-one will hear the an-gels' song, And wish he could join with the
3. Some-one will stand with an ach-ing heart, While Je-sus pro-nounc-es the
4. Some-one will lin-ger with tear-ful eyes, While Christ and His peo-ple as-
5. Some-one will go in-to dark-ness drear, Far off from the Sav-ior and
6. Some-one will en-ter the door of hell, And hear the sad wail-ing no

can-not come;" With sad-ness he'll mourn o'er his sor-row-ful state; Turn'd a-
hap-py throng; With sigh-ing he'll mourn o'er his sor-row-ful state; Turn'd a-
word, "de-part;" With groan-ings he'll mourn o'er his sor-row-ful state; Turn'd a-
cend the skies; With weep-ing he'll mourn o'er his sor-row-ful state; Turn'd a-
all that's dear; With an-guish he'll mourn o'er his sor-row-ful state; Turn'd a-
tongue can tell; With hor-ror he'll mourn o'er his sor-row-ful state, Turn'd a-

FINE   **CHORUS**

way from the beau-ti-ful gate! Turn'd a-way from the beau-ti-ful

D. S.

gate,.......... Turn'd a-way from the beau-ti-ful gate,..........
beau-ti-ful gate,   beau-ti-ful gate,

No. 104 'Tis So Sweet To Trust In Jesus

Mrs. Louisa M. R. Stead

Wm. J. Kirkpatrick

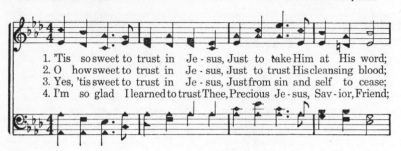

1. 'Tis so sweet to trust in Je-sus, Just to take Him at His word;
2. O how sweet to trust in Je-sus, Just to trust His cleansing blood;
3. Yes, 'tis sweet to trust in Je-sus, Just from sin and self to cease;
4. I'm so glad I learned to trust Thee, Precious Je-sus, Sav-ior, Friend;

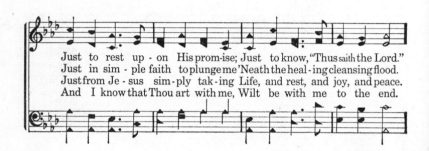

Just to rest up-on His prom-ise; Just to know, "Thus saith the Lord."
Just in sim-ple faith to plunge me 'Neath the heal-ing cleansing flood.
Just from Je-sus sim-ply tak-ing Life, and rest, and joy, and peace.
And I know that Thou art with me, Wilt be with me to the end.

CHORUS

Je-sus, Je-sus, how I trust Him; How I've proved Him o'er and o'er;

Je-sus, Je-sus, Pre-cious Je-sus! O for grace to trust Him more.

No. 105   Softly And Tenderly

W. L. T.   Will L. Thompson

1. Soft - ly and ten - der - ly Je - sus is call - ing, Call - ing for
2. Why should we tar - ry when Je - sus is plead - ing, Plead - ing for
3. Time now is fleet - ing, the mo - ments are pass - ing, Pass - ing from
4. O for the won - der - ful love He has prom - ised, Prom - ised for

you and for me; See on the por - tals He's wait - ing and watch - ing,
you and for me? Why should we lin - ger and heed not His mer - cies,
you and from me; Shad - ows are gath - er - ing, death beds are com - ing,
you and for me; Tho we have sinned He has mer - cy and par - don,

Watch - ing for you and for me. Come home, come
Mer - cies for you and for me?
Com - ing for you and for me.
Par - don for you and for me.

CHORUS

Come home,

home, Ye who are wea - ry, come home, Ear - nest - ly

come home,

ten - der - ly, Je - sus is call - ing, Call - ing, O sin - ner, come home.

No. 106 Rescue The Perishing

Fannie J. Crosby

William H. Doane

1. Res - cue the per - ish-ing, Care for the dy-ing, Snatch them in pit - y from
2. Tho' they are slight-ing Him, Still He is wait-ing, Wait-ing the pen - i - tent
3. Down in the hu-man heart, Crushed by the temp-ter, Feel-ings lie bur-ied that
4. Res - cue the per - ish-ing, Du - ty de-mands it; Strength for thy la - bor the

sin and the grave; Weep o'er the err - ing one, Lift up the fall - en,
child to re-ceive; Plead with them ear - nest - ly, Plead with them gent-ly,
grace can re-store, Touched by a lov - ing heart, Wak-ened by kind-ness,
Lord will pro - vide; Back to the nar-row way Pa - tient - ly win them;

Chorus

Tell them of Je - sus the might - y to save.
He will for-give if they on - ly be - lieve. Res-cue the per-ish-ing,
Chords that are bro - ken will vi-brate once more.
Tell the poor wan-d'rer a Sav - iour has died.

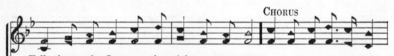

Care for the dy - ing; Je - sus is mer - ci - ful, Je - sus will save.

No. 107 Prepare To Meet Thy God

(From a sermon by Rev. J. F. Haley, July, 1909)

J. H. S. J. H. Stanley

1. Care-less soul, why will you lin-ger, Wand'ring from the fold of God?
2. Why so tho't-less are you stand-ing While the fleet-ing years go by,
3. Hear you not the earn-est plead-ings Of your friends that wish thou well?
4. If you spurn the in-vi-ta-tion Till the Spir-it shall de-part,

Hear you not the in-vi-ta-tion? O pre-pare to meet thy God.
And your life is spent in fol-ly? O pre-pare to meet thy God.
And per-haps be-fore to-mor-row You'll be called to meet your God.
Then you'll see your sad con-di-tion, Un-pre-pared to meet thy God.

CHORUS

Care-less soul,............ O heed the warn-ing,.......... For your
O care-less soul, heed the warn-ing,

life.......... will soon be gone;.......... O how sad.......... to
will soon be gone, O yes, your life will soon be gone; to face the judg-ment,

face the judg-ment,.......... Un-pre-pared...... to meet thy God.
O how sad to face the judg-ment, Un-pre-pared to meet thy God.

No. 108

Whiter Than Snow

James Nicholson

Wm. G. Fischer

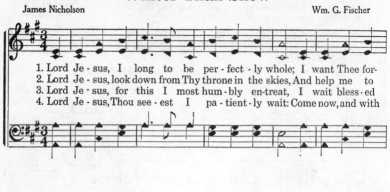

1. Lord Je - sus, I long to be per - fect - ly whole; I want Thee for-
2. Lord Je - sus, look down from Thy throne in the skies, And help me to
3. Lord Je - sus, for this I most hum - bly en-treat, I wait bless - ed
4. Lord Je - sus, Thou see - est I pa - tient - ly wait: Come now, and with

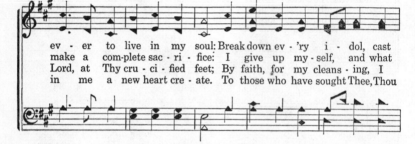

ev - er to live in my soul: Break down ev - 'ry i - dol, cast
make a com-plete sac - ri - fice: I give up my - self, and what
Lord, at Thy cru - ci - fied feet; By faith, for my cleans - ing, I
in me a new heart cre - ate. To those who have sought Thee, Thou

CHORUS

out ev - 'ry foe;
ev - er I know: Now wash me, and I shall be whit-er than snow. Whit-er than
see Thy blood flow:
nev - er said'st no;

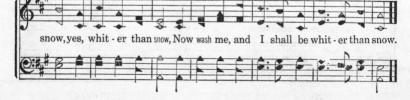

snow, yes, whit - er than snow, Now wash me, and I shall be whit - er than snow.

No. 109   I Surrender All

J. W. Van De Venter   W. S. Weeden

1. All to Je-sus I surren-der, All to Him I free-ly give;
2. All to Je-sus I surren-der, Hum-bly at His feet I bow;
3. All to Je-sus I surren-der, Make me, Sav-ior, whol-ly Thine;
4. All to Je-sus I surren-der, Lord, I give my-self to Thee;
5. All to Je-sus I surren-der, Now I feel the sa-cred flame;

I will ev-er love and trust Him, In His pres-ence dai-ly live.
World-ly plea-sures all for-sak-en, Take me, Je-sus, take me now.
Let me feel the Ho-ly Spir-it, Tru-ly know that Thou art mine.
Fill me with Thy love and pow-er, Let Thy bless-ings fall on me.
Oh, the joy of full sal-va-tion! Glo-ry, glo-ry to His name!

Chorus

I sur-ren-der all, I sur-ren-der all;
I sur-ren-der all. I sur-ren-der all;

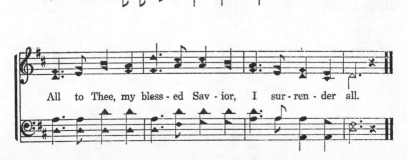

All to Thee, my bless-ed Sav-ior, I sur-ren-der all.

No.110   O Why Not Tonight?

J. Calvin Bushey

1. O do not let the Word de-part, And close thine eyes a-gainst the
2. To-mor-row's sun may nev-er rise, To bless thy long de-lud-ed
3. Our Lord in pit-y lin-gers still, And wilt thou thus His love re-
4. Our bless-ed Lord re-fus-es none Who would to Him their souls u-

light; Poor sin-ner, hard-en not your heart, Be saved, O to-night.
sight; This is the time, O then be wise, Be saved, O to-night.
quite? Re-nounce at once thy stub-born will,
nite; Be-lieve, o-bey, the work is done,

CHORUS

O why not to-night? O
O why not to-night? why not to-night?

why not to-night? Wilt thou be
Why not to-night? why not to-night? Wilt thou be saved? wilt

saved? Then why not to-night?
thou be saved? Then why not, O why not to-night?

No. 111   Near The Cross

"Peace through the blood of his cross."—Col. 1:20.

Fanny J. Crosby   W. H. Doane

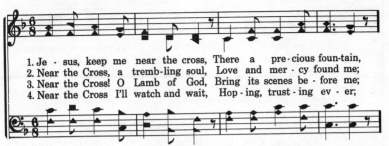

1. Je - sus, keep me near the cross, There a pre - cious foun-tain,
2. Near the Cross, a tremb-ling soul, Love and mer - cy found me;
3. Near the Cross! O Lamb of God, Bring its scenes be - fore me;
4. Near the Cross I'll watch and wait, Hop - ing, trust-ing ev - er;

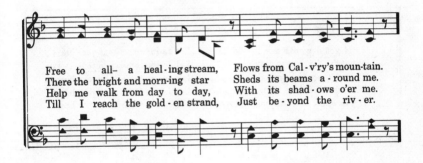

Free to all— a heal - ing stream, Flows from Cal - v'ry's moun-tain.
There the bright and morn-ing star Sheds its beams a - round me.
Help me walk from day to day, With its shad - ows o'er me.
Till I reach the gold - en strand, Just be - yond the riv - er.

CHORUS

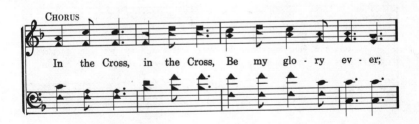

In the Cross, in the Cross, Be my glo - ry ev - er;

Till my rap - tured soul shall find Rest be - yond the riv - er.

Let Jesus Come Into Your Heart

C. H. M.

Mrs. C. H. Morris

1. If you are tired of the load of your sin, Let Je-sus come in-to your heart;
2. If 'tis for pu - ri - ty now that you sigh, Let Je-sus come in-to your heart;
3. If there's a tempest your voice can not still, Let Je-sus come in-to your heart;
4. If friends, once trusted, have proven untrue, Let Je-sus come in-to your heart;
5. If you would join the glad songs of the blest, Let Je-sus come in-to your heart;

If you de-sire a new life to be - gin, Let Je-sus come in-to your heart.
Fountains for cleansing are flowing near by, Let Je-sus come in-to your heart.
If there's a void this world never can fill, Let Je-sus come in-to your heart.
Find what a Friend He will be un-to you, Let Je-sus come in-to your heart.
If you would enter the man-sions of rest, Let Je-sus come in-to your heart.

CHORUS

Just now, your doubt-ings give o'er; Just now, re - ject Him no more;
5th v. Just now, my doubt-ings are o'er; Just now, re - ject-ing no more;

Just now, throw o - pen the door; Let Je-sus come in-to your heart.
Just now, I o - pen the door; And Je-sus comes in-to my heart.

No. 113 Lord, I'm Coming Home

W. J. K.

Wm. J. Kirkpatrick

1. I've wan-dered far a-way from God, Now I'm com-ing home;
2. I've wast-ed man-y pre-cious years, Now I'm com-ing home;
3. I'm tired of sin and stray-ing, Lord, Now I'm com-ing home;
4. My soul is sick, my heart is sore, Now I'm com-ing home;
5. My on-ly hope, my on-ly plea, Now I'm com-ing home;
6. I need His cleans-ing blood, I know, Now I'm com-ing home;

The paths of sin too long I've trod, Lord, I'm com-ing home.
I now re-pent with bit-ter tears, Lord, I'm com-ing home.
I'll trust Thy love, be-lieve Thy word, Lord, I'm com-ing home.
My strength re-new, my hope re-store, Lord, I'm com-ing home.
That Je-sus died, and died for me, Lord, I'm com-ing home.
O wash me whi-ter than the snow, Lord, I'm com-ing home.

CHORUS

Com-ing home, com-ing home, Nev-er-more to roam;

O-pen wide Thine arms of love, Lord, I'm com-ing home.

No. 114

Kneel At The Cross

C. E. M. and
Dwight Brock

Charles E. Moody

1. Kneel at the cross, Christ will meet you there, Come while He waits for you;
2. Kneel at the cross, There is room for all Who would His glo - ry share;
3. Kneel at the cross, Je - sus bids you come, Drink from the fount of love;
4. Kneel at the cross, Give your i - dols up, Look un - to realms a - bove;

List to His voice, Leave with Him your care And be - gin life a - new.
Bliss there a - waits, Harm can ne'er be - fall Those who are an - chored there.
Bliss there a - waits In that heav'n-ly home For all the saved a - bove.
Turn not a - way To life's spark-ling cup; Trust on - ly in His love.

CHORUS

Kneel at the cross, Leave ev - 'ry care;
Kneel at the cross, Kneel at the cross, Leave ev - 'ry care,

ev - 'ry care; Kneel at the
Leave ev - 'ry care; Kneel at the cross,

cross, Je - sus will meet you there.
Kneel at the cross, meet you there.

No. 115 Jesus Is Passing This Way

"He was to pass that way." —Luke 19:4.

Annie L. James

W. H. Doane

Gently, not too fast

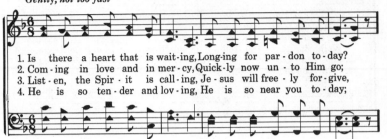

1. Is there a heart that is wait-ing, Long-ing for par-don to-day?
2. Com-ing in love and in mer-cy, Quick-ly now un-to Him go;
3. List-en, the Spir-it is call-ing, Je-sus will free-ly for-give,
4. He is so ten-der and lov-ing, He is so near you to-day;

Rit.

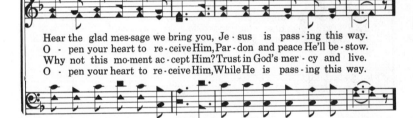

Hear the glad mes-sage we bring you, Je-sus is pass-ing this way.
O - pen your heart to re-ceive Him, Par-don and peace He'll be-stow.
Why not this mo-ment ac-cept Him? Trust in God's mer - cy and live.
O - pen your heart to re-ceive Him, While He is pass-ing this way.

CHORUS

Je-sus is pass-ing this way, ... This way .... to-day; ....
Je-sus is pass-ing, is pass-ing this way, Is pass-ing this way, Is pass-ing to-day;

Rit.

Je-sus is pass-ing this way, ... Is pass-ing this way to-day.
way to-day,

No. 116   Jesus Saves

Priscilla J. Owens

Wm. J. Kirkpatrick

1. We have heard the joy-ful sound: Je-sus saves! Je-sus saves!
2. Waft it on the roll-ing tide, Je-sus saves! Je-sus saves!
3. Sing a-bove the bat-tle strife, Je-sus saves! Je-sus saves!
4. Give the winds a might-y voice, Je-sus saves! Je-sus saves!

Spread the ti-dings all a-round; Je-sus saves! Je-sus saves!
Tell to sin-ners far and wide: Je-sus saves! Je-sus saves!
By His death and end-less life, Je-sus saves! Je-sus saves!
Let the na-tions now re-joice, Je-sus saves! Je-sus saves!

Bear the news to ev-'ry land, Climb the steeps and cross the waves;
Sing, ye is-lands of the sea; Ech-o back, ye o-cean caves;
Sing it soft-ly thru the gloom, When the heart for mer-cy craves;
Shout sal-va-tion full and free; High-est hills and deep-est caves;

On-ward! 'tis our Lord's command; Je-sus saves! Je-sus saves!
Earth shall keep her ju-bi-lee: Je-sus saves! Je-sus saves!
Sing in tri-umph o'er the tomb, Je-sus saves! Je-sus saves!
This our song of vic-to-ry, Je-sus saves! Je-sus saves!

No. 117   I Must Tell Jesus

E. A. H.   E. A. Hoffman

1. I must tell Jesus all of my tri-als; I can-not bear these bur-dens a-lone; In my dis-tress He kind-ly will help me; He ev-er loves and cares for His own.

2. I must tell Jesus all of my trou-bles; He is a kind, com-pas-sion-ate friend; If I but ask Him, He will de-liv-er, Make of my trou-bles quick-ly an end.

3. Tempt-ed and tried I need a great Sav-ior, One who can help my bur-dens to bear; I must tell Je-sus, I must tell Je-sus; He all my cares and sor-rows will share.

4. O how the world to e-vil al-lures me! O how my heart is tempt-ed to sin! I must tell Je-sus, and He will help me O-ver the world the vic-t'ry to win.

Chorus

I must tell Je-sus! I must tell Je-sus! I can-not bear my bur-dens a-lone; I must tell Je-sus! I must tell Je-sus! Je-sus can help me, Je-sus a-lone.

No.118 Is Thy Heart Right With God?

E. A. H.   Elisha A. Hoffman

1. Have thy af - fec-tions been nailed to the cross? Is thy heart right with God?
2. Hast thou do - min - ion o'er self and o'er sin? Is thy heart right with God?
3. Is there no more con-dem - na - tion for sin? Is thy heart right with God?
4. Are all thy pow'rs un - der Je - sus' con-trol? Is thy heart right with God?
5. Art thou now walk-ing in heav-en's pure light? Is thy heart right with God?

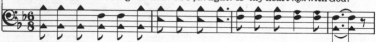

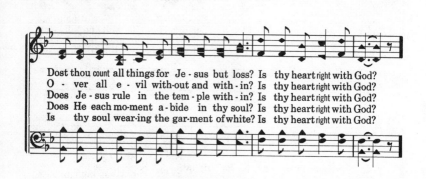

Dost thou count all things for Je - sus but loss? Is thy heart right with God?
O - ver all e - vil with-out and with - in? Is thy heart right with God?
Does Je - sus rule in the tem - ple with - in? Is thy heart right with God?
Does He each mo-ment a - bide in thy soul? Is thy heart right with God?
Is thy soul wear-ing the gar-ment of white? Is thy heart right with God?

Chorus

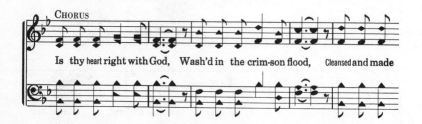

Is thy heart right with God, Wash'd in the crim-son flood, Cleansed and made

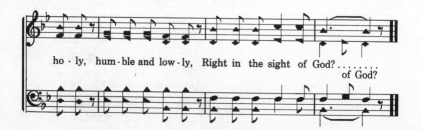

ho - ly, hum - ble and low - ly, Right in the sight of God?........
of God?

Are You Washed In The Blood?

E. A. H.   E. A. Hoffman

1. Have you been to Je-sus for the cleans-ing pow'r? Are you washed in the
2. Are you walk-ing dai-ly by the Sav-ior's side? Are you washed in the
3. When the Bride-groom com-eth will your robes be white, Pure and white in the
4. Lay a-side the gar-ments that are stained with sin, And be washed in the

blood of the Lamb? Are you ful-ly trust-ing in His grace this hour?
blood of the Lamb? Do you rest each mo-ment in the Cru-ci-fied?
blood of the Lamb? Will your soul be read-y for the man-sions bright?
blood of the Lamb; There's a foun-tain flow-ing for the soul un-clean,

CHORUS

Are you washed in the blood of the Lamb? Are you washed in the
Are you washed in the blood of the Lamb?
And be washed in the blood of the Lamb?
O be washed in the blood of the Lamb!   Are you washed

blood,   In the soul-cleans-ing blood of the Lamb?   Are your
     in the blood,   of the Lamb?

gar-ments spot-less, are they white as snow? Are you washed in the blood of the Lamb?

No. 120   Pass Me Not

Fanny J. Crosby

W. H. Doane

1. Pass me not, O gen-tle Sav-ior, Hear my hum-ble cry; While on oth-ers
2. Let me at a throne of mer-cy Find a sweet re-lief; Kneel-ing there in
3. Trust-ing on-ly in Thy mer-it, Would I seek Thy face; Heal my wound-ed,
4. Thou the Spring of all my com-fort, More than life to me, Whom have I on

CHORUS

Thou art call-ing, Do not pass me by.
deep con-tri-tion, Help my un-be-lief. Sav-ior, Sav-ior, Hear my hum-ble
bro-ken spir-it, Save me by Thy grace.
earth be-side Thee? Whom in heav'n but Thee?

cry; While on oth-ers Thou art call-ing, Do not pass me by.

No. 121   I Need Thee Ev'ry Hour

Mrs. Annie S. Hawks

Rev. Robert Lowry

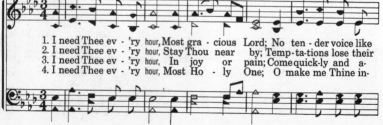

1. I need Thee ev-'ry hour, Most gra-cious Lord; No ten-der voice like
2. I need Thee ev-'ry hour, Stay Thou near by; Temp-ta-tions lose their
3. I need Thee ev-'ry hour, In joy or pain; Come quick-ly and a-
4. I need Thee ev-'ry hour, Most Ho-ly One; O make me Thine in-

I Need Ev'ry Hour

CHORUS

Thine Can peace af - ford.
pow'r When Thou art nigh. I need Thee, O I need Thee; Ev - 'ry hour I
bide, Or life is vain.
deed, Thou bless - ed Son.

need Thee! O bless me now, my Sav - ior, I come to Thee!

No. 122 Nothing But The Blood

R. L.

Robert Lowry

1. What can wash a - way my sin? Noth-ing but the blood of Je - sus;
2. For my par - don this I see– Noth-ing but the blood of Je - sus;
3. Noth - ing can for sin a - tone– Noth-ing but the blood of Je - sus;
4. This is all my hope and peace–Noth-ing but the blood of Je - sus;

FINE

What can make me whole a - gain? Noth-ing but the blood of Je - sus.
For my cleans-ing, this my plea–Noth-ing but the blood of Je - sus.
Naught of good that I have done–Noth-ing but the blood of Je - sus.
This is all my right-eous-ness–Noth-ing but the blood of Je - sus.

D. S.

O pre-cious is the flow That makes me white as snow No oth - er fount I know,

No. 123
Only Trust Him

J. H. S.

J. H. Stockton

1. Come, ev-'ry soul by sin op-pressed, There's mer-cy with the Lord,
2. For Je-sus shed His pre-cious blood, Rich bless-ings to be-stow;
3. Yes, Je-sus is the Truth, the Way, That leads you in-to rest;
4. Come, then, and join this ho-ly band, And on to glo-ry go,

And He will sure-ly give you rest By trust-ing in His word.
Plunge now in-to the crim-son flood That wash-es white as snow.
Be-lieve in Him with-out de-lay, And you are ful-ly blest.
To dwell in that ce-les-tial land, Where joys im-mor-tal flow.

Chorus

{ On-ly trust Him, on-ly trust Him, On-ly trust Him now; }
{ He will save you, He will save you, He will (Omit.......) } save you now.

No. 124
Just As I Am

Charlotte Elliott

William B. Bradbury

1. Just as I am, with-out one plea, But that Thy blood was shed for me,
2. Just as I am, and wait-ing not To rid my soul of one dark blot,
3. Just as I am, tho tossed about With many a con-flict, many a doubt,
4. Just as I am, poor, wretched, blind; Sight, rich-es, heal-ing of the mind,
5. Just as I am—Thou wilt re-ceive, Wilt welcome, pardon, cleanse, relieve;

Just As I Am

And that Thou bidd'st me come to Thee, O Lamb of God, I come! I come!
To Thee whose blood can cleanse each spot, O Lamb of God, I come! I come!
Fight-ings and fears with-in, with-out, O Lamb of God, I come! I come!
Yea, all I need in Thee to find, O Lamb of God, I come! I come!
Be-cause Thy promise I be-lieve, O Lamb of God, I come! I come!

No. 125   **Jesus Paid It All**

Mrs. H. M. Hall   John T. Grape

1. I hear the Sav-ior say, "Thy strength in-deed is small, Child of
2. Lord, now in-deed I find Thy pow'r, and Thine a-lone, Can
3. For noth-ing good have I Where-by Thy grace to claim — I'll
4. And when, be-fore the throne, I stand in Him com-plete, "Je-sus

Chorus

weakness watch and pray, Find in Me thine all in all."
change the lep-er's spots, And melt the heart of stone. Je-sus paid it all,
wash my garments white In the blood of Cal-v'ry's Lamb.
died my soul to save, "My lips shall still re-peat.

All to Him I owe; Sin had left a crimson stain, He washed it white as snow.

No.126   At The Cross

Isaac Watts

R. E. Hudson

1. A - las, and did my Sav - ior bleed, And did my Sov-ereign die;
2. Was it for crimes that I have done, He groaned up - on the tree?
3. Well might the sun in dark-ness hide, And shut His glo - ries in,
4. But drops of grief can ne'er re - pay The debt of love I owe:

Would He de - vote that sa - cred head For such a worm as I?
A - maz - ing pit - y, grace un-known! And love be - yond de - gree!
When Christ, the might - y Mak - er, died For man the crea-ture's sin.
Here, Lord, I give my - self a - way, 'Tis all that I can do!

CHORUS

At the cross, at the cross where I first saw the light, And the

bur - den of my heart rolled a - way,   It was there by
rolled a - way,

faith I re-ceived my sight, And now I am hap - py all the day!

BRING THEM IN

Alexcenah Thomas

W. A. Ogden

1. Hark! 'tis the Shepherd's voice I hear, Out in the des-ert dark and drear,
2. Who'll go and help this Shepherd kind, Help Him the wand'ring ones to find?
3. Out in the des-ert hear their cry, Out on the mountains wild and high;

Call-ing the sheep who've gone astray, Far from the Shepherd's fold a-way.
Who'll bring the lost ones to the fold, Where they'll be sheltered from the cold?
Hark! 'tis the Mas-ter speaks to thee, "Go find My sheep wher-e'er they be,"

Chorus

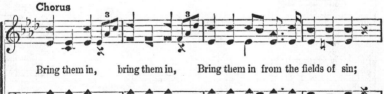

Bring them in, bring them in, Bring them in from the fields of sin;

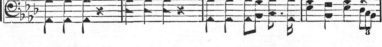

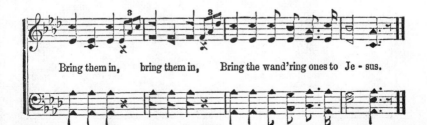

Bring them in, bring them in, Bring the wand'ring ones to Je-sus.

No. 128 Try Jesus

J. R. B., Jr. J. R. Baxter, Jr.

1. You have tried the path of world-ly plea-sure, Sought for peace the
2. Oft your day be-gins with seem-ing glad-ness, Hope is high, your
3. As you walk a-lone in si-lence, think-ing, How you meet with
4. Time is short, the mo-ments swift-ly fly-ing, Mon-ey can-not

world can nev-er give; O be care-ful where you place your trea-sure,
heart with joy is light; Shad-ows fall and dark-ness brings you sad-ness,
fail-ures on the way; Ere your soul in deep de-spair is sink-ing,
buy sweet peace with-in; You are long-ing, seek-ing, grop-ing, sigh-ing,

CHORUS

You need One to teach you how to live.
You need One to ban-ish fears of night. Try Je-sus, He nev-er
You need One whom winds and waves o-bey.
You need One to cleanse you from your sin.

fails, O'er e-vil His love pre-vails, In sun-shine
nev-er fails, for-ev-er-more pre-vails,

or storm-y gales, Try Je-sus, He nev-er fails.
in the storm-y gales, nev-er, nev-er fails.

No. 129   Don't You Want To Go?

Words and Music by James D. Vaughan

1. Don't you want to go to that hap-py home on high? Where the good shall meet yes,
2. Think how man-y pray'rs have been of-fered up for you, Oft-en while you slept dear
3. Time is swift-ly pass-ing, and soon will close the gate, Then your soul must sink in
4. Could you stand in judg-ment if you should die to-day? All that you have writ-ten

meet to part no more, And shall live and reign far a-bove the star-ry sky,
moth-er's tears did flow; Turn and seek sal-va-tion, O to her love be true,
ev-er-last-ing woe, Give your heart to Je-sus, for soon 'twill be too late,
you must face you know Je-sus now is plead-ing, He'll wash your sins a-way,

CHORUS

In that sun-ny clime up-on the gold-en shore.
While your friends are wait-ing, don't you want to go? Don't you want to go?
Moth-er now is wait-ing, don't you want to go?
To that home in glo-ry, don't you want to go?

Don't you want to go? While we plead and pray, make the start to-day; Je-sus bids you

come to that hap-py home, Don't you want to go? Don't you want to go?

No. 130 God Is Calling the Prodigal

C. H. G.

Chas. H. Gabriel

1. God is call-ing the prod-i-gal, come without de-lay, Hear, O hear Him
2. Pa-tient, lov-ing and ten-der-ly still the Fa-ther pleads,
3. Come, there's bread in the house of thy Fa-ther and to spare,

call-ing, call-ing now for thee;   Tho' you've wandered so far from His
                                   Oh! re-turn while the spir-it in
                                   for thee; Lo! the ta-ble is spread and the

pres-ence, come to-day, Hear His lov-ing voice call-ing still.
mer-cy in-ter-cedes,
feast is wait-ing there,   call-ing still.

CHORUS

Call-ing now for thee,   O wea-
Call-ing now for thee,   call-ing now for thee,   Wea-ry prod-i-gal,

-ry prod-i-gal, come;   Call-ing now for
come,   wea-ry prod-i-gal, come; Calling now for thee,

God Is Calling The Prodigal

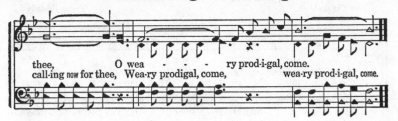

thee,　O wea - - - ry prod-i-gal, come.
call-ing now for thee, Wea-ry prodigal, come,　　wea-ry prod-i-gal, come.

No. 131　O How I Love Jesus

F. Whitfield

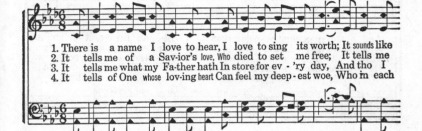

1. There is　a name　I love to hear, I love to sing　its worth; It sounds like
2. It　tells me of　a Sav-ior's love, Who died to set　me free; It tells me
3. It　tells me what my Fa-ther hath In store for ev - 'ry day, And tho I
4. It　tells of One whose lov-ing heart Can feel my deep - est woe, Who in each

CHORUS

mu - sic in mine ear, The sweetest name on earth.
of　His precious blood, The sin-ner's perfect plea.　　O how I love Je-sus,
tread　a darksome path, Yields sunshine all the way.
sor - row bears a part, That none can bear be-low.

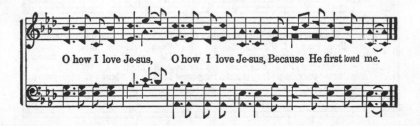

O how I love Je-sus,　O how I love Je-sus, Because He first loved me.

No. 132 — There Is A Fountain

Wm. Cowper

Western Melody

1. There is a foun-tain filled with blood, Drawn from Im-man-uel's veins,
2. The dy-ing thief re-joiced to see That foun-tain in his day;
3. Dear, dy-ing Lamb, thy pre-cious blood Shall nev-er lose its pow'r,
4. E'er since by faith I saw the stream Thy flow-ing wounds sup-ply,
5. Then in a no-bler, sweet-er song I'll sing Thy pow'r to save.

And sin-ners plunged be-neath that flood Lose all their guilt-y stains.
And there may I, tho' vile as He Wash all my sins a-way.
Till all the ransomed church of God Be saved to sin no more.
Re-deem-ing love has been my theme And shall be till I die.
When this poor, lisp-ing, stamm'ring tongue Lies si-lent in the grave.

CHORUS

Lose all their guilt-y stains, Lose all their guilt-y stains,
Wash all my sins a-way, Wash all my sins a-way;
Be saved to sin no more, Be saved to sin no more;
And shall be till I die, And shall be till I die;
Lies si-lent in the grave, Lies si-lent in the grave;

And sin-ners plunged be-neath that flood Lose all their guilt-y stains.
And there may I, though vile as he, Wash all my sins a-way.
Till all the ransomed church of God Be saved to sin no more.
Re-deem-ing love has been my theme And shall be till I die.
When this poor, lisp-ing, stamm'ring tongue Lies si-lent in the grave.

No. 133 Drifting Too Far From The Shore

C. E. M. Chas. E. Moody

1. Out on the per-il-ous deep Where dan-gers si-lent-ly creep
2. To-day the tem-pest rolls high And clouds o'er-shad-ow the sky,
3. Why meet a ter-ri-ble fate When joys a-bun-dant-ly wait?

And storms so vi'-lent-ly sweep
Sure death is hov-er-ing nigh, You are drift-ing too far from
Turn back be-fore it's too late,

the

shore.
peaceful shore.

Chorus

Drift-ing too far from shore, You are
the peace-ful shore,

drift-ing too far from shore; Come to Je-sus to-day, let Him
the peace-ful shore;

show you the way, You are drift-ing too far from shore.
the peace-ful shore.

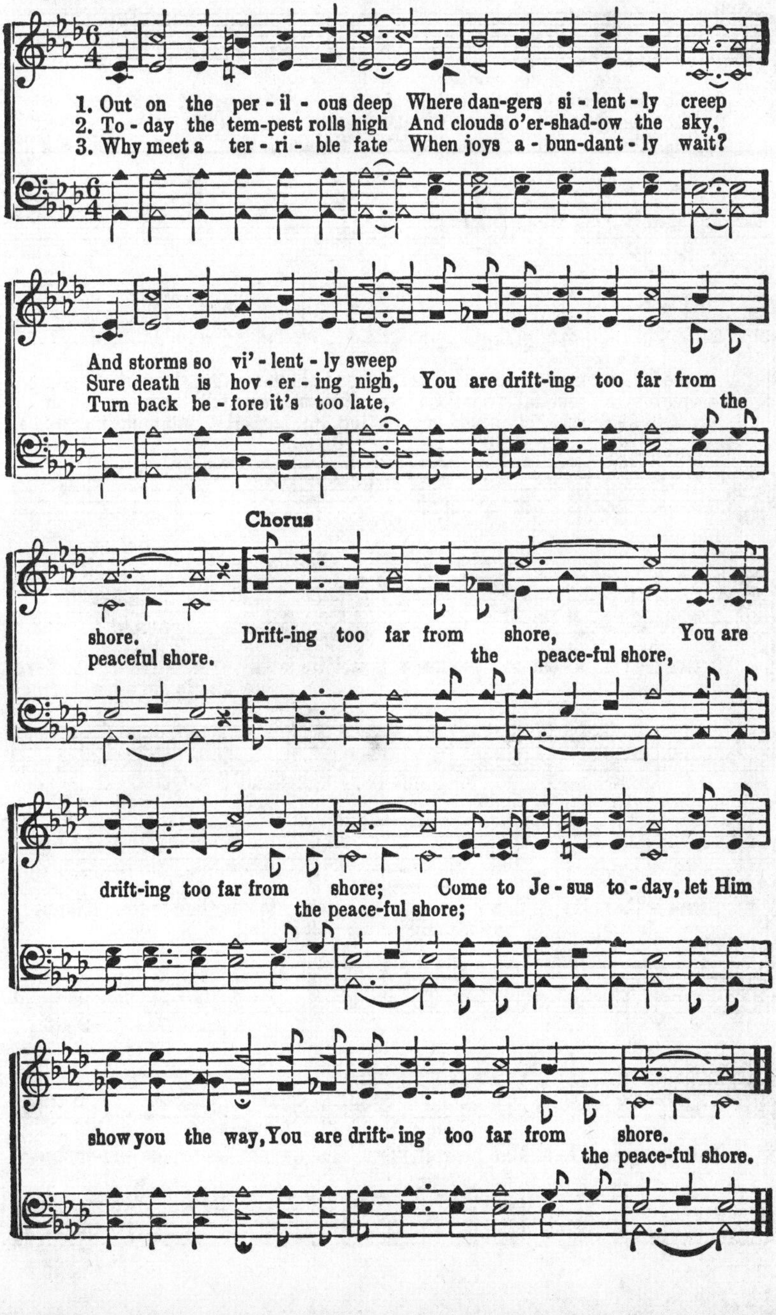

He Is Able to Deliver Thee

W. A. O.

W. A. Ogden

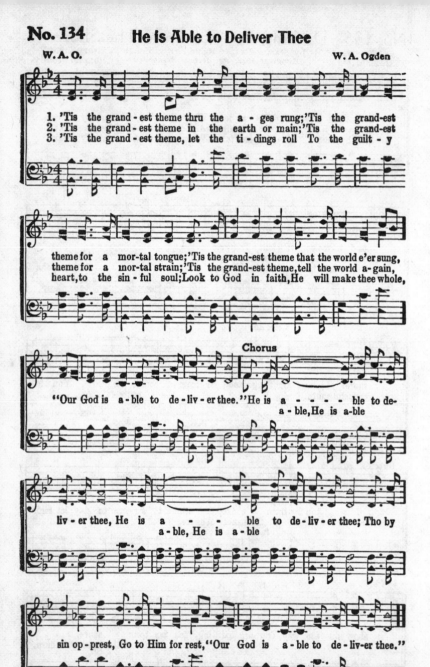

1. 'Tis the grand-est theme thru the a-ges rung;'Tis the grand-est
2. 'Tis the grand-est theme in the earth or main;'Tis the grand-est
3. 'Tis the grand-est theme, let the ti-dings roll To the guilt-y

theme for a mor-tal tongue;'Tis the grand-est theme that the world e'er sung,
theme for a mor-tal strain;'Tis the grand-est theme,tell the world a-gain,
heart,to the sin-ful soul;Look to God in faith,He will make thee whole,

Chorus

"Our God is a-ble to de-liv-er thee."He is a - - - - ble to de-
a-ble,He is a-ble

liv-er thee, He is a - - - ble to de-liv-er thee; Tho by
a-ble, He is a-ble

sin op-prest, Go to Him for rest,"Our God is a-ble to de-liv-er thee."

No. 135 Where Is My Boy To-Night?

R. L.

Rev. R. Lowry

1. Where is my wan-dering boy to-night The boy of my tenderest care,
2. Once he was pure as morn-ing dew, As he knelt at his moth-er's knee;
3. O could I see you now, my boy, As fair as in old-en time,
4. Go for my wan-dering boy to-night; Go search for him where you will;

The boy that was once my joy and light, The child of my love and prayer?
No face was so bright, no heart more true, And none was so sweet as he.
When prat-tle and smile made home a joy, And life was a mer-ry chime!
But bring him to me with all his blight, And tell him I love him still.

CHORUS Not too fast

O where is my boy to-night? O where is my boy to-night?

My heart o'er-flows, for I love him he knows; O where is my boy to-night?

Precious Name

MRS. LYDIA BAXTER.

W. H. DOANE.

1. Take the name of Je-sus with you, Child of sor-row and of woe;
2. Take the name of Je-sus ev-er, As a shield from ev-'ry snare;
3. At the name of Je-sus bow-ing, Fall-ing prostrate at His feet,

It will joy and com-fort give you, Take it then wher-e'er you go.
If temp-ta-tions 'round you gath-er, Breathe that ho-ly name in pray'r.
King of kings in heav'n we'll crown Him, When our jour-ney is com-plete.

CHORUS.

Precious name, O how sweet! Hope of earth and joy of heav'n,
Precious name, O how sweet,

Precious name, O how sweet— Hope of earth and joy of heav'n.
Precious name, O how sweet, how sweet,

No. 137

HE LOVES ME

Rev. Isaac Watts

AIR.

1. A-las! and did my Sav-ior bleed? And did my sov-'reign die?
2. Was it for crimes that I have done He groaned up-on the tree?
3. Thus might I hide my blush-ing face While His dear cross ap-pears;
4. But drops of grief can ne'er re-pay The debt of love I owe;

HE LOVES ME

Fine

Would He de-vote that sa-cred head For such a worm as I?
A-maz-ing pit-y! grace un-known! And love be-yond de-gree!
Dis-solve my heart in thank-ful-ness, And melt mine eyes to tears.
Here, Lord, I give my-self a-way, 'Tis all that I can do.

D.S.—He gave Him-self to die for me, Be-cause He loved me so.

Refrain

D.S.

He loves me, He loves me, He loves me, this I know, I know;

No. 138 SAVIOR, MORE THAN LIFE

Fanny J. Crosby   W. H. Doane

1. Sav-ior, more than life to me, I am cling-ing, cling-ing close to Thee;
2. Thru this changing world be-low, Lead me gen-tly, gen-tly as I go;
3. Let me love Thee more and more, Till this fleet-ing, fleet-ing life is o'er;

Fine

Let Thy pre-cious blood applied, Keep me ev-er, ev-er near Thy side.
Trust-ing Thee, I can-not stray, I can nev-er, nev-er lose my way.
Till my soul is lost in love, In a bright-er, bright-er world a-bove.

D.S.—May Thy ten-der love to me Bind me clos-er, clos-er, Lord, to Thee.

Refrain

D.S.

Ev-'ry day,   ev-'ry hour,   Let me feel Thy cleansing pow'r;
Ev-'ry day and hour, ev-'ry day and hour,

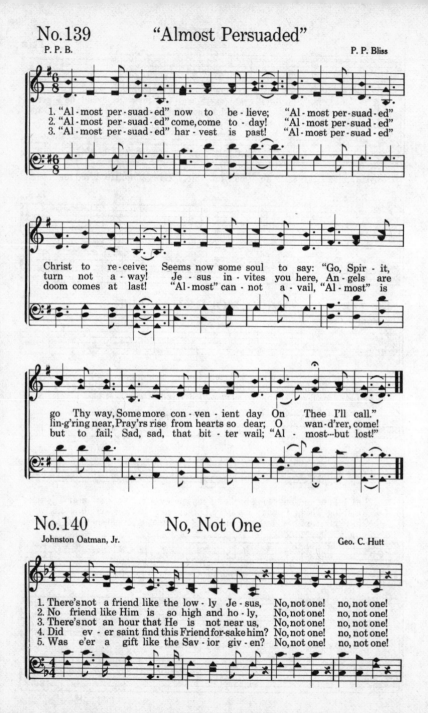

No. 139   "Almost Persuaded"

P. P. B.

P. P. Bliss

1. "Al-most per-suad-ed" now to be-lieve; "Al-most per-suad-ed"
2. "Al-most per-suad-ed" come, come to-day! "Al-most per-suad-ed"
3. "Al-most per-suad-ed" har-vest is past! "Al-most per-suad-ed"

Christ to re-ceive; Seems now some soul to say: "Go, Spir-it,
turn not a-way! Je-sus in-vites you here, An-gels are
doom comes at last! "Al-most" can-not a-vail, "Al-most" is

go Thy way, Some more con-ven-ient day On Thee I'll call."
lin-g'ring near, Pray'rs rise from hearts so dear; O wan-d'rer, come!
but to fail; Sad, sad, that bit-ter wail; "Al-most---but lost!"

No. 140   No, Not One

Johnston Oatman, Jr.

Geo. C. Hutt

1. There's not a friend like the low-ly Je-sus, No, not one! no, not one!
2. No friend like Him is so high and ho-ly, No, not one! no, not one!
3. There's not an hour that He is not near us, No, not one! no, not one!
4. Did ev-er saint find this Friend for-sake him? No, not one! no, not one!
5. Was e'er a gift like the Sav-ior giv-en? No, not one! no, not one!

No, Not One

None else could heal all our soul's dis-eas-es, No, not one! no, not one!
And yet no friend is so meek and low-ly, No, not one! no, not one!
No night so dark but His love can cheer us, No, not one! no, not one!
Or sin-ner find that He would not take him, No, not one! no, not one!
Will He re-fuse us a home in heav-en? No, not one! no, not one!

D.S.-There's not a friend like the low-ly Je-sus, No, not one! no, not one!

CHORUS

Je-sus knows all a-bout our struggles, He will guide till the day is done;

No. 141   **Where He Leads Me**

E. W. Blandly

J. S. Norris

1. I can hear my Sav-ior call-ing, I can hear my Sav-ior call-ing,
2. I'll go with Him thru the gar-den, I'll go with Him thru the gar-den,
3. I'll go with Him thru the judg-ment, I'll go with Him thru the judg-ment,
4. He will give me grace and glo-ry, He will give me grace and glo-ry,

Cho.-Where He leads me I will fol-low, Where He leads me I will fol-low,

I can hear my Sav-ior call-ing, "Take thy cross and fol-low, fol-low me."
I'll go with Him thru the gar-den, I'll go with Him, with Him all the way.
I'll go with Him thru the judg-ment, I'll go with Him, with Him all the way.
He will give me grace and glo-ry, And go with me, with me all the way.

Where He leads me I will fol-low, I'll go with Him, with Him all the way.

Come Unto Me

Charles P. Jones

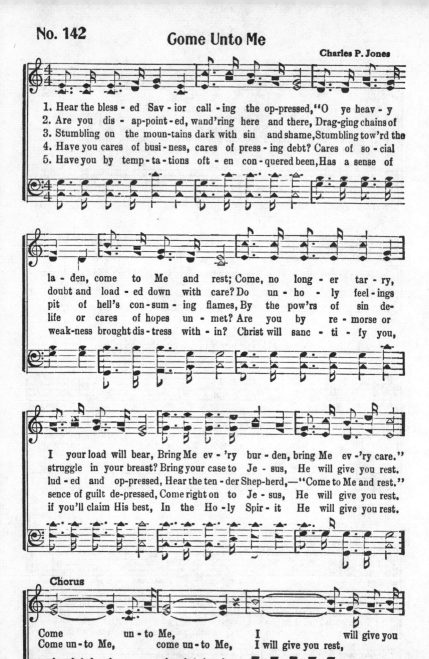

1. Hear the bless-ed Sav-ior call-ing the op-pressed, "O ye heav-y
2. Are you dis-ap-point-ed, wand'ring here and there, Drag-ging chains of
3. Stumbling on the moun-tains dark with sin and shame, Stumbling tow'rd the
4. Have you cares of busi-ness, cares of press-ing debt? Cares of so-cial
5. Have you by temp-ta-tions oft-en con-quered been, Has a sense of

la-den, come to Me and rest; Come, no long-er tar-ry,
doubt and load-ed down with care? Do un-ho-ly feel-ings
pit of hell's con-sum-ing flames, By the pow'rs of sin de-
life or cares of hopes un-met? Are you by re-morse or
weak-ness brought dis-tress with-in? Christ will sanc-ti-fy you,

I your load will bear, Bring Me ev-'ry bur-den, bring Me ev-'ry care."
struggle in your breast? Bring your case to Je-sus, He will give you rest.
lud-ed and op-pressed, Hear the ten-der Shep-herd,—"Come to Me and rest."
sence of guilt de-pressed, Come right on to Je-sus, He will give you rest.
if you'll claim His best, In the Ho-ly Spir-it He will give you rest.

Chorus

Come un-to Me, I will give you
Come un-to Me, come un-to Me, I will give you rest,

Come Unto Me

No. 143   I am Trusting, Lord, in Thee

William McDonald

William G. Fischer

1. I am com-ing to the cross; I am poor and weak and blind;
2. Long my heart has sighed for Thee; Long has e - vil reigned with - in;
3. Here I give my all to Thee; Friends and time and earth - ly store;
4. In the prom - is - es I trust; Now I feel the blood ap - plied;
5. Je - sus comes! He fills my soul! Per - fect - ed in Him I am;

Cho.- I am trust - ing, Lord, in Thee, Bless-ed Lamb of Cal - va - ry;

D.C. for Chorus

I am count - ing all but dross; I shall full sal - va - tion find.
Je - sus sweet - ly speaks to me, "I will cleanse you from all sin."
Soul and bod - y Thine to be, Whol - ly Thine for - ev - er - more.
I am pros - trate in the dust; I with Christ am cru - ci - fied.
I am ev - 'ry whit made whole: Glo - ry, glo - ry to the Lamb!

Hum-bly at Thy cross I bow, Save me, Je - sus, save me now.

No. 144   Glory to His Name

Rev. E. A. Hoffman

Rev. J. H. Stockman

1. Down at the cross where my Savior died, Down where for cleansing from sin I cried; There to my heart
2. O precious fountain that saves from sin, I am so glad I have entered in; There Jesus saves
3. Come to this fountain, so rich and sweet; Cast thy poor soul at the Savior's feet; Plunge in today

D. S.—There to my heart

Fine   **Refrain**   **D. S.**

was the blood applied; Glory to His name.
me and keeps me clean;
and be made complete;   Glory to His name,   Glory to His name;

was the blood applied; Glory to His name.

No. 145 IF SALVATION HAD NOT BEEN FREE.

S. L.

SHERMAN LONG.

1. If the price of sal-va-tion were sil-ver and gold, All the
2. All the poor of my peo-ple, thus speak-eth the Lord, "They shall
3. Oh, what love and com-pas-sion, was made man-i-fest, When He
4. "It is fin-ished" oh, hear Him so ten-der-ly say, When He

poor of this world would be lost; But the Sav-iour who loved us, in
feast on the fat of the land"; Ev-'ry one who will trust me, be-
gave up His life on the tree; Sure de-liv-'rance He brought to the
gave up His all on the tree; Thus the plan of sal-va-tion was

CHORUS.

mer-cy we're told, Paid the price on the cru-el cross.
liev-ing my word, Shall be strengthened and made to stand. Oh, Lord, **oh,**
poor and oppressed, And sal-va-tion to all is free.
made on that day, Full sal-va-tion for you and me.

Lord, what could I have done, If sal-va-tion had not been free?

"God so loved the world, He gave His on-ly Son," Thus making a way for me.

No. 146 — Come and Dine

Words and melody by C. C. Widmeyer

S. H. Bolton

1. Je - sus has a ta - ble spread Where the saints of God are fed,
2. The dis - ci - ples came to land, Thus o - bey - ing Christ's command,
3. Soon the Lamb will take His bride To be ev - er at His side,

He in - vites His chos - en peo - ple "Come and dine;" With His man - na
For the Mas - ter called un - to them "Come and dine;" There they found their
All the host of heav - en will as - sem - bled be; O, 'twill be a

He doth feed And sup - plies our ev - 'ry need; O 'tis sweet to sup with
hearts' de - sire, Bread and fish up - on the fire; Thus He sat - is - fies the
glo - rious sight, All the saints in spot - less white; And with Je - sus they will

CHORUS.

Je - sus all the time!
hun - gry ev - 'ry time. "Come and dine," the Mas - ter call - eth, "Come and
feast e - ter - nal - ly.

dine;"
O come and dine;
You may feast at Je - sus' ta - ble all the

Come and Dine

time; O come and dine; He who fed the mul-ti-tude, Turned the

wa-ter in-to wine, To the hun-gry call-eth now, "Come and dine."

No. 147 Break Thou the Bread of Life

Mary Ann Lathbury   William F Sherwin

1. Break Thou the bread of life, Dear Lord, to me, As Thou didst
2. Bless Thou the truth, dear Lord, To me— to me— As Thou didst
3. Thou art the bread of life, O Lord, to me, Thy ho-ly
4. O send Thy spir-it, Lord, Now un-to me, That He may

break the loaves Be-side the sea; Be-yond the sa-cred page
bless the bread By Gal-i-lee; Then shall all bond-age cease,
Word, the truth That sav-eth me; Give me to eat and live
touch my eyes, And make me see: Show me the truth con-cealed

I seek Thee, Lord; My spir-it pants for Thee, O liv-ing Word.
All fet-ters fall; And I shall find my peace, My All in all.
With Thee a-bove; Teach me to love Thy truth, For Thou art love.
With-in Thy Word, And in Thy book re-vealed I see the Lord.

No. 148 The Way Of The Cross Leads Home

Jessie Brown Pounds

Chas. H. Gabriel

1. I must needs go home by the way of the cross, There's no oth-er
2. I must needs go on in the blood-sprinkled way, The path that the
3. Then I bid fare-well to the way of the world, To walk in it

way but this; I shall ne'er get sight of the Gates of Light
Sav- ior trod, If I ev - er climb to the heights sub-lime,
nev- er-more; For my Lord says "Come" and I seek my home,

CHORUS

If the way of the cross I miss.
Where the soul is at home with God.
Where He waits at the o - pen door.

The way of the cross leads
home, The way of the cross leads home; It is
leads home, leads home;

sweet to know, as I on-ward go, The way of the cross leads home.

No. 149 The Blood That Stained The Old Rugged Cross

A. E. B.   Albert E. Brumley

Very Slow

1. On the cross of Cal-va-ry our bless-ed Sav-ior died, Gave His
2. To the cross, the rug-ged cross they nailed His pre-cious hands And in
3. What an aw-ful death He died to par-don you and me, All a-

life to save the world from loss; In His pain and ag-o-ny, for ev-'ry
death He ful-ly paid the cost, There is par-don in His love for ev-'ry
lone in ag-o-ny He tossed, And a world once lost in sin can now be

FINE   CHORUS

sin to hide, Shed the
one that stands For the blood that stained the old rug-ged cross. 'Twas His
whol-ly free By the

blood, His precious blood that stained the old rug-ged cross, 'Twas His love that paid the

D.S.

aw-ful cost; O soul so far a-stray come and plunge to-day In the

No. 150 Down On My Knees

M. L. Mosie Lister

Down On My Knees

Old Satan tried to say the Bi-ble was a lie, That
Old Sa-tan tried to tell me the Bi-ble was a lie, That

Je-sus did not care, And I would die; Stayed down
Je-sus did not love me And I was doomed to die; But I stayed on my

on my knees, 'way down on my knees, He took my bur-den a-way.
knees, stayed on my knees, Je-sus took my burden a-way.

No. 151 **Standin' in the Need of Prayer**

by B. B. E.
ad lib.

Copyright, 1925, by B. B. Edmiaston
Used by permission

by B. B. EDMIASTON

1. Not my fath-er, nor my moth-er, but it's me, O Lord, Standin' in the need of prayer;
2. Not the prophet, nor the preacher, but it's me, O Lord, Standin' in the need of prayer;
3. Not the people who are shoutin', but it's me, O Lord, Standin' in the need of prayer;
4. Not the oth-er man in dan-ger, but it's me, O Lord, Standin' in the need of prayer;

Not my sis-ter, nor my broth-er, but it's me, O Lord, Standin' in the need of prayer.
Not the deacon, not the teacher, but it's me, O Lord, Standin' in the need of prayer.
Not the members I am doubtin', but it's me, O Lord, Standin' in the need of prayer.
Not my neighbor, nor the stranger, but it's me, O Lord, Standin' in the need of prayer.

Invisible Hands

Words and Music by Buddy Kaye, Bill Harrington,
Frank Stanton and Fred Patrick

1. In - vis - i - ble hands.........are wait-ing to guide you,
2. In - vis - i - ble hands.........will keep you from dan - ger,

In - vis - i - ble hands.......will show you the way, will show you the way;
In - vis - i - ble hands.......will keep you from harm, will keep you from harm;

Have faith in the Lord,.........He's al - ways be - side you,
Tho' you may have sinned,.........God wel - comes a stran - ger,

So pray and be- lieve, and help you'll re-ceive from in - vis - i - ble hands.

FINE

CHORUS

In - vis - i - ble hands,

Are wait-ing to guide you,

in - vis - i - ble

Invisible Hands

D.S.

are al-ways be-side you, So pray and be-lieve, and help you'll re-ceive
hands,

No. 153 — My Desire

Words and Music by Thomas A. Dorsey

1. It's my de-sire to do some good thing ev-'ry day, It's my de-sire
2. It's my de-sire to bring some wand'rer to the fold It's my de-sire
3. It's my de-sire to teach some sin-ner how to pray, It's my de-sire
4. It's my de-sire to see His face when life is done, It's my de-sire

to help the fall-en by the way; It's my de-sire to bring back
to shel-ter some one from the cold; It's my de-sire to do His
to help some trav-'ler find the way; It's my de-sire to lift up
to meet the Fa-ther and the Son; It's my de-sire to hear Him

those who've gone a-stray,
will as I am told, It's my de-sire to be like the Lord.
Je-sus ev-'ry day,
say "My child well done,"

No. 154 When God Dips His Love in my Heart

C. D. CLEAVANT DERRICKS

1. When God dips His pen of love in my heart And writes my soul a message He wants me to know, His Spirit all divine fills this sinful soul of mine, When God dips His love in my heart.

2. Sometimes tho' the way is dreary, dark and cold, And some unburdened sorrow keeps me from the goal, I go to God in prayer, I can always find Him there (hallelujah!) To whisper sweet peace to my soul.

3. He walked every step up Calv'ry's rugged way To give His life completely, and bring a better day; My life was steeped in sin, but in love He took me in, His blood washed away ev'ry stain.

REFRAIN

Well, I said I wouldn't tell it to a living soul How He bro't salvation when He made me

When God Dips His Love in My Heart

whole, But I found I couldn't hide such love as Je-sus did im-part;

'Cause it makes me
Laugh and it makes me cry,
then it
sets my sin-ful soul on fire, hal-le-lu-jah! When God dips His love in my heart.

No. 155 Where Could I Go?

J. B. C.   J. B. Coats

1. Liv - ing be - low in this old sin-ful world, Hardly a com-fort can af-ford;
2. Neighbors are kind, I love them ev-'ry one, We get a - long in sweet ac-cord;
3. Life here is grand with friends I love so dear, Comfort I get from God's own word;

Cho.- Where could I go, O where could I go, Seek-ing a ref-uge for my soul?

D. C. for Chorus

Striv-ing a - lone to face temptations sore,
But when my soul needs manna from a-bove, Where could I go but to the Lord?
Yet when I face the chill-ing hand of death,

Needing a friend to save me in the end, Where could I go but to the Lord?

No.156 Blessed Assurance

Fanny J. Crosby

Mrs. J. F. Knapp

1. Bless-ed as-sur-ance, Je-sus is mine! O what a fore-taste of
2. Per-fect sub-mis-sion, per-fect de-light, Vi-sions of rap-ture now
3. Per-fect sub-mis-sion, all is at rest, I in my Sav-ior am

glo-ry di-vine! Heir of sal-va-tion, pur-chase of God,
burst on my sight; An-gels de-scend-ing, bring from a-bove
hap-py and blest; Watch-ing and wait-ing, look-ing a-bove,

CHORUS

Born of His Spir-it, washed in His blood.
Ech-oes of mer-cy, whis-pers of love. This is my sto-ry,
Filled with His good-ness, lost in His love.

this is my song, Prais-ing my Sav-ior all the day long; This is my

sto-ry, this is my song, Prais-ing my Sav-ior all the day long.

No. 157   Just Because He Loved Me So

J. E. French

No. 158 I DREAMED I SEARCHED HEAVEN FOR YOU

MARY ETHEL WIESS · JAMES D. VAUGHAN

Very Slow, with expression.

1. I dreamed I had gone to that cit-y, That cit-y where
2. I looked on both sides of the riv-er, That flows thro' the
3. I asked of ten thou-sand sweet an-gels, Have you seen this be-

nev-er comes night, And I saw the bright an-gels in glo-ry, I
cit-y of God, I searched thro' bright mansions celestial, And
lov'd one? pray tell, Have you met in the bright courts of heaven, That

saw the fair mansions of light; I gazed for long, long years of rap-ture,
streets of gold pavement I trod; The fa-ces of saints by the mil-lion,
one whom on earth we loved well; They shook their heads sadly and told me,

On the face of my Sav-ior so true, And I sang with the
I scanned in my yearn-ing to see, That face I had
That they had not seen you, and then, I knew that some-

ser-a-phim ho-ly,— Then I dreamed I searched heaven for you.
cher-ished so fond-ly,— The face that had grown dear to me.
where in the dark-ness, You wandered, lost, lost in sin.

I Dreamed I Searched Heaven for You

CHORUS.

I dreamed I searched heav-en for you, ... Searched vain-ly thru
for you,

heav-en for you; .... Friend, won't you pre-pare to
for you;

meet me up there? Lest we should search heav-en for you.

No. 159

THE SWEETEST NAME!

Frederick Whitfield.   Lowell Mason.

1. There is a name I love to hear, I love to speak its worth;
2. It tells me of a Sav-iour's love, Who died to set me free;
3. Je-sus! the name I love so well, The name I love to hear!
4. This name shall shed its fra-grance still A-long this thorn-y road;

It sounds like mu-sic in mine ear—The sweet-est name on earth.
It tells me of His pre-cious blood, The sin-ner's per-fect plea.
No saint on earth its worth can tell, No heart con-ceive how dear.
Shall sweetly smoothe the rug-ged hill That leads me up to God.

No. 160 The Promised Land

Samuel Stennett

Arr. by R. M. McIntosh

1. On Jordan's storm-y banks I stand And cast a wish-ful eye
2. O'er all those wide ex-tend-ed plains Shines one e-ter-nal day,
3. No chill-ing wind nor pois-'nous breath Can reach that health-ful shore,
4. When shall I reach that hap-py place And be for-ev-er blest?

To Ca-naan's fair and hap-py land, Where my pos-ses-sions lie.
There God, the Son, for-ev-er reigns, And scat-ters night a-way.
Sick-ness and sor-row, pain and death, Are felt and feared no more.
When shall I see my Fa-ther's face And in His bos-om rest?

D.S.-O who will come and go with me? I am bound for the prom-ised land.

CHORUS

I am bound for the prom-ised land, I am bound for the prom-ised land;
prom-ised land,

No. 161 My Faith Looks Up To Thee

Ray Palmer

Lowell Mason

1. My faith look up to Thee, Thou Lamb of Cal-va-ry, Sav-ior di-vine; Now hear me
2. May Thy rich grace im-part Strength to my faint-ing heart, My zeal in-spire; As Thou hast
3. While life's dark maze I tread, And grief a-round me spread, Be Thou my guide; Bid dark-ness

while I pray, Take all my sins a-way, O let me from this day Be whol-ly Thine!
died for me, O may my love to Thee Pure warm, and change-less be, A liv-ing fire!
turn to day, Wipe sor-row's tears a-way, Nor let me ev-er stray From Thee a-side.

No. 162 Take Time To Be Holy

W. D. Longstaff

Geo. C. Stebbins

1. Take time to be ho-ly, Speak oft with thy Lord; A-bide in Him
2. Take time to be ho-ly, The world rush-es on; Spend much time in
3. Take time to be ho-ly, Be calm in thy soul; Each tho't and each

al-ways, And feed on His word. Make friends of God's chil-dren; Help
se-cret With Je-sus a-lone. A-bid-ing in Je-sus, Like
mo-tive Be-neath His con-trol. Thus led by His Spir-it To

those who are weak, For-get-ting in noth-ing His bless-ings to seek.
Him thou shalt be; Thy friends in thy con-duct His like-ness shall see.
foun-tains of love, Thou soon shall be fit-ted For serv-ice a-bove.

No. 163 Nearer My God To Thee

Lowell Mason

1. Near-er, my God, to Thee, Near-er to Thee; E'en tho' it be a cross
2. Tho' like a wan-der-er, The sun gone down, Dark-ness be o-ver me,
3. Or if, on joy-ful wing, Cleav-ing the sky, Sun, moon and stars for-got,

D.S.-Near-er, my God, to Thee,

FINE

D.S.

That rais-eth me, Still all my song shall be, Near-er, my God, to Thee!
My rest a stone, Yet in my dreams I'd be, Near-er, my God, to Thee!
Up-ward I fly, Still all my song shall be, Near-er, my God, to Thee!

Near-er, to Thee!

No. 164 Leaning On The Everlasting Arms

A. E. Hoffman

A. J. Showalter

1. What a fel-low-ship, what a joy di-vine, Lean-ing on the ev-er-
2. O how sweet to walk in this pil-grim way, Lean-ing on the ev-er-
3. What have I to dread, what have I to fear, Lean-ing on the ev-er-

last-ing arms; What a bless-ed-ness, what a peace is mine,
last-ing arms; O how bright the path grows from day to day,
last-ing arms: I have bless-ed peace with my Lord so near,

CHORUS

Lean-ing on the ev-er-last-ing arms. Lean - ing,
Lean-ing on the ev-er-last-ing arms.
Lean-ing on the ev-er-last-ing arms. Lean-ing on Je-sus

lean - - ing, Safe and se-cure from all a-larms;
lean-ing on Je-sus,

Lean - ing, lean - ing, Lean-ing on the ev-er-last-ing arms.
Lean-ing on Je-sus, lean-ing on Je-sus,

No. 165　God Can Do Anything But Fail

I. F. S.

Ira F. Stanphill
Arr. by Al Smith

1. God can do an-y-thing, an-y-thing, an-y-thing, God can
2. He can save, He can cleanse, He can keep, and He will, God can

do an-y-thing, but fail. He's the Al-pha and O-
do an-y-thing, but fail.

me-ga, the Be-gin-ning and the End. He's the fair-est of ten

thou-sand to my soul. God can do an-y-thing, an-y-

thing, an-y-thing, God can do an-y-thing, but fail.

No. 166

This Little Light of Mine

V. O. Fossett

1. This lit-tle light of mine, Yes,
2. Hide it un-der a bush-el? No, I'm gon-na let it shine;
3. Won't let Sa - tan blow it out,
4. Let it shine till Je-sus comes,

This lit-tle light of mine, Yes,
Hide it un-der a bush-el? No, I'm gon-na let it
Won't let Sa - tan blow it out,
Let it shine till Je-sus comes,

shine; Let it shine, let it shine, let it shine.

No. 167

The B-I-B-L-E

V. O. Fossett

The B - I - B - L - E, Yes, that's the book for me; I

stand a - lone on the Word of God, The B - I - B - L - E.

No. 168 Let The Beauty Of Jesus Be Seen

George L. Johnson   Cleavant Derricks

1. Let the beau-ty of Je-sus be seen in me, All His won-der-
2. When your bur-den is heav-y and hard to bear, When your neigh-bors
3. When some-bod-y has been so un-kind to you, Some word spo-ken
4. From the dawn of the morn-ing to close of day, In ex-am-ple

ful pas-sion and pur-i-ty, May His Spir-it di-vine all my
re-fuse all your load to share; When you're feel-ing so blue, don't know
that pierc-es you thru, and thru, Think how He was be-guiled, spat up-
in deeds and in all you say; Lay your gifts at His feet, ev-er

be-ing re-fine, Let the beau-ty of Je-sus be seen in me.
just what to do, Let the beau-ty of Je-sus be seen in you.
on and re-viled, Let the beau-ty of Je-sus be seen in you.
strive to keep sweet, Let the beau-ty of Je-sus be seen in you.

No. 169   Only Believe

P. R.   Paul Rader

On-ly be-lieve, on-ly be-lieve, All things are pos-si-ble, on-ly be-lieve;

On-ly be-lieve, on-ly be-lieve, All things are pos-si-ble, on-ly be-lieve.

No. 170 — Give Me Oil In My Lamp

V. O. Fossett

Give me oil in my lamp, oil in my lamp, Give me oil in my lamp, I pray;

Give me oil in my lamp, keep me shining in the camp Until the break of day.

No. 171 — Down In My Heart

V. O. Fossett

1. I have sweet joy, joy, joy, joy, down in my heart,
2. I have the peace that dwell-eth down in my heart,
3. I have the love of Je-sus down in my heart,
4. For there's no con-dem-na-tion down in my heart,

Down in my heart, down in my heart, I have sweet
Down in my heart, down in my heart, I have the
Down in my heart, down in my heart, I have the
Down in my heart, down in my heart, For there's no

joy, joy, joy, joy, down in my heart, Down in my heart to stay.
peace that dwelleth down in my heart, Down in my heart to stay.
love of Je-sus down in my heart, Down in my heart to stay.
con-dem-na-tion down in my heart, Down in my heart to stay.

No. 172   Happy All the Way

Copyright, 1952, by Stamps-Baxter Music & Printing Co.
in "Evangelistic Songs"

V. O. Fossett

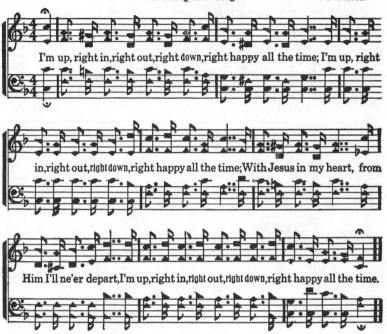

I'm up, right in, right out, right down, right happy all the time; I'm up, right

in, right out, right down, right happy all the time; With Jesus in my heart, from

Him I'll ne'er depart, I'm up, right in, right out, right down, right happy all the time.

No. 173   We'll Be Dwelling Together

Copyright, 1952, by Stamps-Baxter Music & Printing Co
in "Evangelistic Songs"

O. Fossett

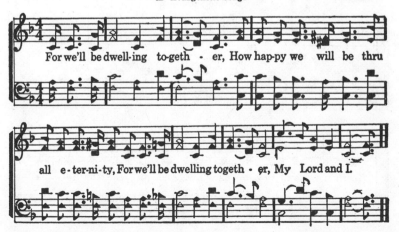

For we'll be dwell-ing to-geth - er, How hap-py we will be thru

all e-ter-ni-ty, For we'll be dwelling togeth - er, My Lord and I.

The Birds Upon the Tree-Tops

in "Evangelistic Songs"

V. O. Fossett

The birds up-on the tree-tops sing their song, The an-gels chant the cho-rus all day long; The flow-ers in the gar-den blend their hue, So why shouldn't I, why shouldn't you praise Him too?

Send a Great Revival

Anon

W. H. Doane

In my heart, in my heart, Send a great re-viv-al; Teach me how to watch and pray, And to read the Bi-ble.

No. 176   Good Morning To You!

Brightly.

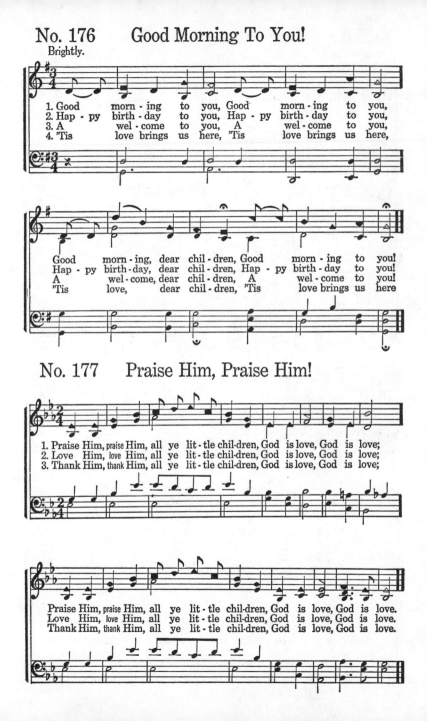

1. Good morn - ing to you, Good morn - ing to you,
2. Hap - py birth - day to you, Hap - py birth - day to you,
3. A wel - come to you, A wel - come to you,
4. 'Tis love brings us here, 'Tis love brings us here,

Good morn - ing, dear chil - dren, Good morn - ing to you!
Hap - py birth - day, dear chil - dren, Hap - py birth - day to you!
A wel - come, dear chil - dren, A wel - come to you!
'Tis love, dear chil - dren, 'Tis love brings us here

No. 177   Praise Him, Praise Him!

1. Praise Him, praise Him, all ye lit - tle chil-dren, God is love, God is love;
2. Love Him, love Him, all ye lit - tle chil-dren, God is love, God is love;
3. Thank Him, thank Him, all ye lit - tle chil-dren, God is love, God is love;

Praise Him, praise Him, all ye lit - tle chil-dren, God is love, God is love.
Love Him, love Him, all ye lit - tle chil-dren, God is love, God is love.
Thank Him, thank Him, all ye lit - tle chil-dren, God is love, God is love.

No. 178   Feeling Grand

L. G. P.   Luther G. Presley

1. Ev-er since I met the Sav-ior, I'm feel-ing grand,   Ev-er
2. Now I walk and talk with Je-sus,   Now I
3. I'm so glad I got re-li-gion,   I'm so
4. In my heart the fire is burn-ing,   feel-ing grand, In my

since I met the Sav-ior, I'm feel-ing grand;   Feel-ing grand be-
walk and talk with Je-sus,
glad I got re-li-gion,
heart the fire is burn-ing,   feel-ing grand;

cause He loves me, for the Sun that shines a-bove me, Feel-ing grand, feel-ing

grand, feel-ing grand; Feel-ing grand on Monday, Tuesday, Wednesday, Thursday,

Fri-day and Sat-ur-day, Praise the Lord, on Sun-day too, I'm feel-ing grand.

Do Lord

V. O. Fossett

1. I've got a home in glo-ryland that out-shines the sun, I've got a
2. I took Je-sus as my Sav-ior, you take Him, too, I took

home in glo-ry land that out-shines the sun; I've got a home in
Je-sus as my Sav-ior, you take Him, too; I took Je-sus

glo-ry land that out-shines the sun, Way be-yond the blue.
as my Sav-ior, you take Him, too, While He's call-ing you.

D.S.- Way be-yond the blue.

CHORUS

Do Lord, O do Lord, O do re-mem-ber me, Do Lord, O do Lord, O

do re-mem-ber me; Do Lord, O do Lord, O do re-mem-ber me,

No. 180 — God Is Love

I be-lieve, you be-lieve, God is good and God is love. We
That He lives in heav'n a-bove,

know, we know, For the Bi-ble tells us so. We know He loves His
We know, we know,

CHORUS

chil-dren, for that is plain to see, It was be-cause He loved us

that He went to Cal-va-ry: I be-lieve, you be-lieve, God is good

and God is love, We know, we know, For the Bi-ble tells us so.
We know, we know,

Aint It A Shame

As Sung by Cook & Whitworth

1. Aint it a shame to work on Sunday, Aint it a shame, a work - ing shame, Aint it a shame to work on Sunday, Aint it a shame, (a work - ing shame,) Aint it a shame to work on Sunday,

2. Aint it a shame to joy - ride Sunday, Aint it a shame, a joy - rid-ing shame, Aint it a shame to joy - ride Sunday, Aint it a shame, (a joy - rid-ing shame,) Aint it a shame to joy - ride Sunday,

3. Aint it a shame to gos-sip on Sunday, Aint it a shame, a gos-sip-ing shame, Aint it a shame to gossip on Sunday, Aint it a shame, (a gos-sip-ing shame,) Aint it a shame to gos-sip on Sunday,

4. Aint it a shame to lie on Sunday, Aint it a shame, a ly - ing shame, Aint it a shame to lie on Sunday, Aint it a shame, (a ly - ing shame,) Aint it a shame to lie on Sunday,

When you got Mon - day, Tues - day and Wednesday, And you got

Thurs-day, Fri - day and Sat - ur - day, Aint it a shame.

rit.

Everybody Ought To Love Jesus

Harry Dixon Loes

Ev-'ry-bod-y ought to love Je-sus, Je - sus, Je - sus; He
Jesus Christ, the wonderful Savior,

died on the cross to save us from sin, Ev-'rybod-y ought to love Je - sus.

No. 183 **WE'LL OUTSHINE THE SUN.**

Furnished by C. F. W.

Arr. by A. F. I.

1. If Je - sus leads this ar - my, We will out - shine the sun, We will
2. If we keep on a pray-ing, We will out - shine the sun, We will

out-shine the sun, We will outshine the sun; If Je - sus leads this ar - my,
out-shine the sun, We will outshine the sun; If we keep on a pray-ing,

We will out-shine the sun, And we'll walk the gold-en streets on high.
We will out-shine the sun, And we'll walk the gold-en streets on high.

3 If we keep on believing, etc.
4 If we stay clean and humble, etc.
5 If Jesus keeps us polished, etc.
6 If we keep on a-shouting, etc.
7 Keep winning souls for Jesus, And we'll outshine the sun, etc.

No. 184 He Knows How

James Rowe.

Chas. W. Vaughan.

1. He knows how, yes, He knows how, Heav'n-ly joys I'm
   Je - sus knows ex - act - ly how,

hav - ing here and now; O praise Him, All the way to glo - ry,
   with Him

I shall tell my sto - ry, Je-sus keeps me hap-py, for He knows how.

No. 185 Little Ones Like Me

Geo. B. Holsinger

1. Je - sus, when He left the sky, And for sin-ners came to die, In His mer - cy
2. Moth-ers then the Sav - ior sought, In the plac - es where He taught, Un - to Him their
3. Did the Sav - ior say them nay! No, He kind - ly bade them stay; Suf - fered none to
4. Chil - dren then should love Him now, Strive His ho - ly will to do, Pray to Him, and

FINE   CHORUS   D.S.

passed not by Lit-tle ones like me.
child - ren bro't, Lit-tle ones like me.   Lit-tle ones like me,   Lit-tle ones like me;
turn a - way Lit-tle ones like me.
praise Him too, Lit-tle ones like me.

No. 186 Say Amen

L. G. P. Luther G. Presley

Ev'ry-body on the Lord's side, Say A-men, Ev'ry-body on the Lord's side, Say A-men;

Je-sus wants to hear it, Now and then, Ev'ry-bod-y on the Lord's side, Say A-men.

No. 187 Love My Jesus, Too

L. G. P. Luther G. Presley

1. Well, I love some-bod-y, And I know just who;
2. Well, I love my play-mates, Like I ought to do;
3. Well, I love the flow-ers, Red, and white, and blue;

Love my Moth-er, love my Dad-dy, Love my Je-sus, too.
Love the world that is so pret-ty, Love my Je-sus, too.
Love the bird-ies in the tree-tops, Love my Je-sus, too.

CHORUS

Love, love, love, love, Love my Mother, love my Dad-dy, Love my Je-sus, too.
Love, love, love, love, Love the world that is so pret-ty, Love my Je-sus, too.
Love, love, love, love, Love the bird-ies in the treetops, Love my Je-sus, too.

No. 188   Talk About Jesus

L. G. P.   Luther G. Presley

1. If you want to talk a-bout some-bod-y,
2. If you want to tell someone a se-cret, Tell you what you ought to do;
3. If you want to give some-bod-y glo-ry,

Talk a-bout Je-sus, talk a-bout Je-sus, Tell a-bout His love so true.
Tell it to Je-sus, tell it to Je-sus, He's the One to tell it to.
Give it to Je-sus, give it to Je-sus, He's the One to give it to.

No. 189   Doing Little Things For Jesus

W. A. L.   W. A. Lowery

Do-ing lit-tle things for Je-sus, Do-ing lit-tle things for Je-sus,

Je-sus sees them, and He adds them up each day; Do-ing lit-tle things for Je-sus,

Do-ing lit-tle things for Je-sus, Hop-ing to live with Him some day.
hap-py day.

No. 190 Every Time I Feel The Spirit

Fred S. Martin

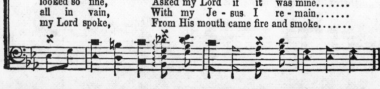

Ev - 'ry time I feel the spir - it Mov-in'
Ev - 'ry time I feel the spir-it

in my heart, I will pray, Ev - 'ry
Mov - in' in my heart,........ I will pray,

time I feel the spir - it Mov - in' in my
Ev - 'ry time I feel the spir-it Mov-in'

heart, I will pray.
in my heart,........ I will pray.

1. Chil - ly wa - ters
2. All a - round me
3. Sa - tan tempts me
4. On the moun - tain

FINE

D. C.

run - nin' cold, Chill the bod - y not the soul........
looked so fine, Asked my Lord if it was mine........
all in vain, With my Je - sus I re - main........
my Lord spoke, From His mouth came fire and smoke........

No. 191 I'm Living In Sunlight Now

J. R. B., Jr. J. R. Baxter, Jr.

1. Hap-py am I and cloud-less the sky, No lon-ger to sin I bow;
2. Shadows have passed, I've gladness at last, My Sav-ior has taught me how
3. Je-sus, my King, whose praises I sing, Is crown-ing with joy my brow;

The dark-ness is gone, I'm fac-ing the dawn, I'm liv-ing in sun-light now.
To car-ry my load and trav-el life's road, I'm liv-ing in sun-light now.
'Tis glo-ry each day to fol-low His way, I'm liv-ing in sun-light now.

Chorus

Liv-ing in sun-light now,............
in the bless-ed sun-light now, I'm Liv-ing in

sun-light now;.............
in the bless-ed sun-light now; I've Noth-ing to fear when

Je-sus is near, I'm liv-ing in sun-light now.....................
in the bless-ed sun-light now.

No. 192 Love Will Roll The Clouds Away

James Rowe

Samuel W. Beazley

1. Sweet is the tho't when a storm is sweep-ing, Mak-ing such a drear-y day;
2. Sweet is the tho't when our bur-dens bend us, When the tempt-er would dis-may;
3. Sweet is the tho't when we reach the riv-er, When for light and cheer we pray,

Safe are our souls in the Mas-ter's keep-ing; Love will roll the clouds a-way.
Je - sus will strength-en and de - fend us; Love will roll the clouds a-way.
Je - sus our Friend will be with us ev - er; Love will roll the clouds a-way.

CHORUS

Love will roll the clouds a - way,
Love will roll . . . . the clouds a - way, ... Love will

Love will roll the clouds a-way; Trust and be true, all is
roll . . . . the clouds a - way; . . . .

well with you; Love will roll the clouds a - way. . . . .
Love will roll . . . . the clouds a - way. (the clouds a - way.)

Lean On His Arm

F. L. Eiland

W. M. Ramsey

1. Lean on the mighty arm of Je-sus, Hide in the hol-low of His hand;
2. Lean on the mighty arm of Je-sus, Wait you not for the morn-ing dawn;
3. Lean on the mighty arm of Je-sus, For 'tis the on-ly ref-uge sure;
4. Lean on the mighty arm of Je-sus, And of His bound-less mer-cy share;

'Neath His pro-tect-ing wings a-bide you, Firm on the Rock of A-ges stand.
Ev-'ning of life may come and find you, And with your strength and cour-age gone.
Let not an-oth-er's in-vi-ta-tion, Now from this hope, your soul al-lure,
Drink of the ev-er-liv-ing fount-ain, Down by the Rock of A-ges there,

CHORUS

Lean on His arm, ... Hide in the hol-low of His hand!
Lean on His arm, His ev-er-last-ing arm,

Lean on His arm, ... Firm on the Rock of A-ges stand.
Lean on His arm, His ev-er-lasting arm,

No. 194   On The Jericho Road

D. S. McC.

Not too fast

Donald S. McCrossan
Arr. by Luther G. Presley

1. As you trav-el a - long .... on the Jer - i - cho road, ...
2. On the Jer - i - cho road .... blind Bar-tim-ae-us sat, ...
3. O   broth-er to you .... this   mes-sage I bring, ...

Does the world seem all wrong .... and heav-y your load? ....
His   life was a void, ... so emp-ty and flat; ....
Tho   hope may be gone, ... He'll cause you to sing; ....

Just bring it to Christ, ... your sins all con-fess, ...
But Je - sus ap-peared, ... one word bro't him sight, ...
At   Je - sus' com-mand, ... sin's shack-les must fall, ...

On the Jer - i - cho road .... your heart He will bless
On the Jer - i - cho road .... Christ ban-ished his night ....
On the Jer - i - cho road .... will you answer His call? ....

CHORUS

On the Jer-i-cho road .... there's room for just two,
On the Jer-i-cho road .... there's room for just two, ...

On The Jericho Road

No more and no less, Just Jesus and you;
No more and no less . . . . just Je-sus and you;

Each bur-den He'll bear, ... each sor-row He'll share, ...
each bur-den He'll bear each sor-row He'll share,

There's nev-er a care for Je-sus is there.
There's nev-er a care . . . . for Je-sus is there. . . . .

No. 195 The Old-Time Religion

Arr. by A. J. S.

Cho.-'Tis the old - time re - li-gion,'Tis the old - time re - li-gion,'Tis the old
1. Makes me love   ev - 'ry-bod-y, Makes me love   ev - 'ry-bod-y, Makes me love
2. It   was good   for our moth-ers, It was good   for our moth-ers, It was good

time re - li-gion, It's good e-nough for me.
ev - 'ry-bod - y, It's good e-nough for me.
for our moth-ers, It's good e-nough for me.

3. It has saved all our fathers,
4. It will save all our children,
5. It was good for Paul and Silas,
6. It will do when I am dying,
7. It will take us all to heaven,

No. 196 I'm Bound For The Kingdom

Copyright, 1951, by Tennessee Music & Printing Co.
in "Songtime Extras"

M. L.

Mosie Lister

1. You may ask me where I'm head-ed, you may ask me where I'm bound,
2. Well, I'm go-ing to a coun-try where they say we'll nev-er die,

Well, I'm go-ing to a coun-try 'cross the sea; And I know I'll
'Twill be end-less joy and glo-ry there for me; Yes, I know I'll

have a man-sion, and I know I'll have a crown. Well, I'm bound for the
live for-ev-er in that cit-y in the sky.

King-dom of the free.

CHORUS

Yes, I'm bound for the King-dom

of the bless-ed and the free, And my Je-sus soon is com-ing aft-er

I'm Bound For The Kingdom

me, aft-er me; There is noth-ing to com-pare with the glo-ry

o-ver there, Yes, I'm bound for the King-dom of the free.

No. 197   Cleanse Me

Edwin Orr

Maori Melody
Arr. Otis L. McCoy

1. Search me, O God, and know my heart to-day, Try me, O
2. I praise Thee Lord, for cleans-ing me from sin, Ful-fill Thy
3. Lord, take my life, and make it whol-ly Thine, Fill my poor
4. O Ho-ly Ghost, re-vi-val comes from Thee, Send a re-

Sav-ior, know my thoughts, I pray; See if there be some wick-ed
Word, and make me pure with-in; Fill me with fire, where once I
heart with Thy great love di-vine; Take all my will, my pas-sion,
vi-val,- start the work in me; Thy Word de-clares Thou wilt sup-

way in me; Cleanse me from ev-'ry sin, and set me free.
burned with shame, Grant my de-sire to mag-ni-fy Thy name.
self and pride, I now sur-ren-der, Lord, in me a-bide.
ply our need, For bless-ing now, O Lord, I hum-bly plead.

No. 198 He's the Lily of the Valley

Arr. Otis Deaton

O. D.

1. Ev - 'ry-bod - y ought to know,............... Ev - 'ry-bod - y ought to
1. Ev - 'ry-bod - y ought to tell,............... Ev - 'ry-bod - y ought to
2. Ev - 'ry-bod - y ought to bring,............... Ev - 'ry-bod - y ought to
2. Ev - 'ry-bod - y ought to sing,............... Ev - 'ry-bod - y ought to

know,............... Ev - 'ry-bod - y ought to know,...............
tell,............... Ev - 'ry-bod - y ought to tell,...............
bring,............... Ev - 'ry-bod - y ought to bring,...............
sing,............... Ev - 'ry-bod - y ought to sing,...............

1.
who Je-sus is, who my bless-ed Je-sus is; who Je - sus is, who my blessed Savior is.
a soul to Him, bring a dying soul to Him; glad praise to Him, hap-py prais-es to my Lord.

2.

CHORUS

He's the Lil - y of the Val - - - - - ley,
Je - sus is the Lil - y of the Val-ley,

He's the Bright and Morn-ing Star;
He's the Shin-ing Star sent down from heav-en;

He's the Lily of the Valley

He's the fair-est of Ten thou - - - - - sand,
He's the fair-est of the man - y thou-sands,

Ev-'ry-bod-y ought to know.
ev-'ry-bod-y ought to know.

No. 199   Heaven

J. T. C.   John. T. Cook

1. There'll be   no shad-ows in heav-en, No cares to dark-en the way;
2. There'll be   no weep-ing in heav-en, No sor-row ev - er can come;
3. There'll be   no part-ing in heav-en, For time and space count no more;

God's face, with light will be shin-ing, Thru-out the e - ter-nal day.
God's hand, all tear-drops will ban-ish, In   heav-en, our home, sweet home.
God's love will there re - u - nite us; With dear ones who've gone be-fore.

D. S. - Con - tent-ment reign-eth   e - ter - nal, The half has ne'er yet been told.

CHORUS   **D.S.**

'Twill all be joy up in heav-en, Beau-ti-ful cit-y of gold;

No. 200　　　Hide Thou Me

L. R. Tolbert

Thoro Harris

1. Some-times I feel dis-cour-aged, and think my life in vain,
2. Some-times it seems I dare not go one step far-ther on,
3. O what a Friend is Je-sus, sure An-chor for my soul,

I'm tempt-ed then to mur-mur, and of my lot com-plain;
And from my heart all cour-age has dis-ap-peared and gone;
So ten-der, true and gra-cious, I'm safe in His con-trol;

But when I think of Je-sus, and all He's done for me,
But, I re-mem-ber Je-sus, and all His love for me,
My help in time of dan-ger, my strong de-fense is He,

Then, I cry, O Rock of A-ges, Hide Thou me.
Then, I cry, O Rock of A-ges, Hide Thou me.
O Thou bless-ed Rock of A-ges, Hide Thou me.

CHORUS

O Rock of A-ges, Hide Thou me, No oth-er Ref-uge,

Hide Thou Me

have I but Thee, When life's dark vale I wan-der, Far, far from

Thee; Then, I cry, O Rock of A-ges, Hide Thou me.

No. 201   I Need The Prayers

"and pray one for another . . . The effectual fervant prayer of a righteous man availeth much."—James 5:16.

J. D. V.   James D. Vaughan

With feeling

1. I need the prayers of those I love, While trav-'ling o'er life's rug-ged way, That
2. I need the prayers of those I love, To help me in each try-ing hour, To
3. I want my friends to pray for me, To hold me up on wings of faith, That

FINE CHORUS

I may true and faith-ful be, And live for Je-sus ev-'ry day.
bear my tempt-ed soul to Him, That He may keep me by His pow'r.   I want my friends to
I may walk the nar-row way, Kept by our Fa-ther's glo-rious grace.

D.S.-I need the prayers of those I love.

pray for me, To bear my tempt-ed soul a-bove, And in-ter-cede with God for me;

No. 202 I've Never Been Sorry

A. E. B. Albert E. Brumley

1. Ev - er since Je-sus saved and pardoned I have been singing ev - 'ry day,
2. All the day long I sing the sto - ry, prais-ing Him for His won - drous love,
3. Bright-ly the star of hope is shin-ing, mak-ing my pathway bright-er grow,

Praise the Lord, bless-ed, ho - ly name;
I've nev - er been sor-ry that I trust-ed His name;

Thru the dark shadows He is with me, lead-ing me on the up-ward way,
Sure - ly I know a home is wait-ing, beau-ti - ful home in heav'n a - bove,
Nev - er a thot of sad re - pin-ing, Je - sus is with me, this I know,

Praise the Lord, bless-ed, ho - ly name.
I've nev-er been sorry that I trust-ed His name.

CHORUS

Praise the Lord, bless-ed, ho-ly name;
I've nev-er been sor-ry that I trust-ed His name,

I've Never Been Sorry

All the way He's ex-act-ly the same,
Ev'ry mo-ment I find Him ex-act-ly the same,

Ev - 'ry day since the Sav-ior came,
My soul has been sing-ing since the Sav-ior came,

- Praise the Lord, bless-ed, ho - ly name.
I've nev-er been sor-ry that I trust-ed His name.

No. 203   Amazing Grace

John Newton   Wm. Walker

1. A - maz-ing grace how sweet the sound, That saved a wretch like me!
2. 'Twas grace that taught my heart to fear, And grace my fears re - lieved;
3. Thru man - y dan-gers, toils and snares, I have al - read - y come;
4. When we've been there ten thosand years, Bright shin-ing as the sun,

I once was lost, but now am found; Was blind, but now I see.
How pre-cious did that grace ap-pear, The hour I first be-lieved.
'Tis grace that bro't me safe thus far, And grace will lead me home.
We've no less days to sing God's praise, Than when we first be-gun.

No. 204 When The Roll Is Called Up Yonder

James M. Black

James M. Black

1. When the trum-pet of the Lord shall sound, and time shall be no more, And the
2. On that bright and cloud-less morn-ing when the dead in Christ shall rise, And the
3. Let us la-bor for the Mas-ter from the dawn till set-ting sun, Let us

morn-ing breaks, e-ter-nal, bright and fair; When the saved of earth shall gath-er
glo-ry of His res-ur-rec-tion share; When His chos-en ones shall gath-er
talk of all His won-drous love and care; Then when all of life is o-ver

o-ver on the oth-er shore, And the roll is called up yon-der, I'll be there.
to their home be-yond the skies, And the roll is called up yon-der, I'll be there.
and our work on earth is done, And the roll is called up yon-der, I'll be there.

CHORUS

When the roll . . . . is called up yon - - - der, When the
When the roll is called up yon-der, I'll be there,

roll . . . . is called up yon - - - der, When the roll . . . . is called up
When the roll is called up yon-der, I'll be there, When the roll is called up

When The Roll Is Called Up Yonder

yon-der, When the roll is called up yon-der, I'll be there.

No. 205   I'll Be Satisfied

Joe H. Pannell

T. N. Pannell

1. When my soul is sing-ing in that prom-ised land a-bove,
2. Liv-ing in a cit-y where the soul shall nev-er die,
3. When I meet the ran-somed o-ver on the gold-en shore,

I'll be sat-is-fied; Prais-ing Christ the Sav-ior for re-
There to meet with loved ones, nev-er
There I'll join the an-gels sing-ing

D.S.—When my soul is rest-ing in the

FINE CHORUS

deem-ing grace and love, I'll be sat-is-fied. I'll be sat-is-
more to say good-by,
prais-es ev-er-more,

pres-ence of the Lord, I'll be sat-is-fied;

D.S.

fied, (sat-is-fied,) I'll be sat-is-fied; (sat-is-fied;)

When Morning Comes

1. Tri - als dark on ev - 'ry hand, and we can - not un - der-stand All the
2. We are oft - en des - ti - tute of the things that life de-mands, Want of
3. Temp - ta-tions, hid-den snares, oft - en take us un - a - wares, And our

ways that God will lead us to that bless - ed prom-ised land; But He'll
shel - ter and of food, thirst - y hills and bar - ren land; But we're
hearts are made to bleed, for each thought-less word or deed; And we

guide us with His eye, and we'll fol-low till we die, We will un-der-stand it
trust-ing in the Lord, and ac - cord-ing to His word, We will un-der-stand it
won-der why the test, when we try to do our best, But will un-der-stand it

D. S. - We will un-der-stand it

Fine   Chorus

bet - ter by and by.
bet - ter by and by.   By and by when the morn - ing comes, All the saints of
bet - ter by and by.

bet - ter by and by.

D. S.

God are gath-er - ing home, We will tell the sto - ry how we've o - ver-come,

No. 207 Sweet By And By

S. Fillmore Bennett

Jos. P. Webster

1. There's a land that is fair-er than day, And by faith we can see it a-
2. We shall sing on that beau-ti-ful shore The me-lo-di-ous songs of the
3. To our boun-ti-ful Fa-ther a-bove, We will of-fer our trib-ute of

far; For the Fa-ther waits o-ver the way, To pre-pare us a
blest, And our spir-its shall sor-row no more, Not a sigh for the
praise, For the glo-ri-ous gift of His love, And the bless-ings that

CHORUS

dwell-ing place there. In the sweet by and by, We shall
bless-ing of rest.
hal-low our days. In the sweet by and by,

meet on that beau-ti-ful shore, In the sweet by and
by and by, In the sweet

by, We shall meet on that beau-ti-ful shore.
by and by,

No. 208   Farther Along

W. B. S.

Rev. W. B. Stevens
J. R. Baxter, Jr.

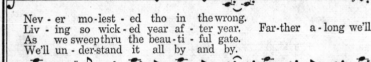

1. Tempt-ed and tried we're oft made to won-der Why it should be thus
2. When death has come and tak-en our loved ones, It leaves our home so
3. Faith-ful till death said our lov-ing Mas-ter, A few more days to
4. When we see Je-sus com-ing in glo-ry, When He comes from His

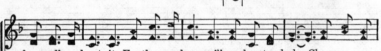

all the day long, While there are oth-ers liv-ing a-bout us,
lone-ly and drear; Then do we won-der why oth-ers pros-per,
la-bor and wait; Toils of the road will then seem as noth-ing,
home in the sky; Then we shall meet Him in that bright man-sion,

CHORUS

Nev-er mo-lest-ed tho in the wrong.
Liv-ing so wick-ed year af-ter year.   Far-ther a-long we'll
As we sweep thru the beau-ti-ful gate.
We'll un-der-stand it all by and by.

know all a-bout it, Far-ther a-long we'll un-der-stand why; Cheer up, my

broth-er, live in the sunshine, We'll understand it all by and by.

No. 209 Precious Memories

J. B. F. W. and
Lonnie B. Combs

J. B. F. Wright

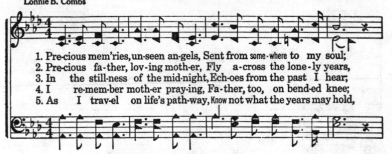

1. Pre-cious mem'ries, un-seen an-gels, Sent from some-where to my soul;
2. Pre-cious fa-ther, lov-ing moth-er, Fly a-cross the lone-ly years,
3. In the still-ness of the mid-night, Ech-oes from the past I hear;
4. I re-mem-ber moth-er pray-ing, Fa-ther, too, on bend-ed knee;
5. As I trav-el on life's path-way, Know not what the years may hold,

How they lin-ger, ev - er near me, And the sa-cred past un-fold.
And old home scenes of my child-hood, In fond mem - o - ry ap-pears.
Old - time sing-ing, glad-ness bring-ing, From that love-ly land some-where.
Sun is sink-ing, shad-ows fall - ing, But their pray'rs still fol-low me.
As I pon-der, hope grows fon-der, Pre-cious mem-'ries flood my soul.

CHORUS

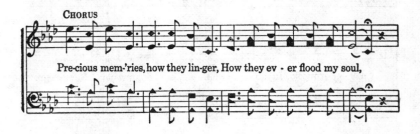

Pre-cious mem-'ries, how they lin-ger, How they ev - er flood my soul,

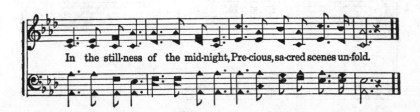

In the still-ness of the mid-night, Pre-cious, sa-cred scenes un-fold.

No. 210 Where We'll Never Grow Old

(To my father and mother.—J. C. M.)

J. C. M.

Copyright, 1930, by Jas. C. Moore

Jas. C. Moore

1. I have heard of a land on the far a-way strand, 'Tis a beau-ti-ful
2. In that beau-ti-ful home where we'll nev-er-more roam, We shall be in that
3. When our work here is done and our life-crown is won, And our trou-bles and

home of the soul; Built by Je-sus on high, there we nev-er shall die,
sweet by and by; Hap-py praise to the King thru e-ter-ni-ty sing,
tri-als are o'er; All our sor-row will end, and our voic-es will blend,

Chorus

'Tis a land where we nev-er grow old. Nev-er grow old,
'Tis a land where we nev-er shall die.
With the loved ones who've gone on be-fore. where we'll

nev-er grow old, In a land where we'll nev-er grow old; Nev-er grow

old, nev-er grow old, In a land where we'll nev-er grow old.
where we'll

Wonderful City

C. D. Williams

1. O - ver the riv - er, shin - ing for - ev - er, There is a
2. Home of the sag - es, saints of the a - ges, Mar - tyrs and
3. Has - ten to - mor - row, end of all sor - row, When this glad

cit - y, I know, Won - der - ful sto - ry! man - sions of glo - ry
an - gels of light; Free of all sad - ness, cit - y of glad - ness,
home I shall see; When with my Sav - ior, hap - py for - ev - er,

Chorus

Wait - ing for pil - grims be - low.
Al - ways so peace - ful and bright! Won - der - ful cit - y; beau - ti - ful
Rest - ing a - bove I shall be.

cit - y, Built with - out hands by our King; Mar - vel - ous

cit - y, glo - ri - ous cit - y, Where we for - ev - er shall sing.

No. 212 How Beautiful Heaven Must Be

A. S. Bridgewater and
Dwight Brock

A. P. Bland

1. We read of a beauti-ful heav-en, Pre-pared for the pure and the free;
2. In heav-en, no droop-ing nor pin-ing, No wish-ing for else-where to be;
3. I'm long-ing to go to fair heav-en, To be with the hap-py and free;
4. The an-gels so sweet-ly are sing-ing, Up there by the beau-ti-ful sea;

These truths in God's word He has giv - en, How beau-ti-ful heav-en must be.
God's light is for - ev - er there shin - ing, How beau-ti-ful heav-en must be.
To spend the long a-ges in sing - ing, How beau-ti-ful heav-en must be.
Sweet chords from their gold harps are ring - ing, How beau-ti-ful heav-en must be.

CHORUS

How beau-ti-ful heav-en must be, Sweet home of the hap-py and free;
must be,

Fair ha-ven of rest for the wea - ry, How beau-ti-ful heav-en must be.

No. 213 Shall We Gather At The River

R. L.

Robert Lowry

1. Shall we gath-er at the riv-er, Where bright an-gel feet have trod,
2. On the mar-gin of the riv-er, Dash-ing up its sil-ver spray,
3. Ere we reach the shin-ing riv-er, Lay we ev-'ry bur-den down;
4. Soon we'll reach that sil-ver riv-er, Soon our pil-grim-age shall cease;

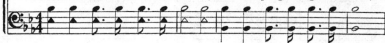

With its crys-tal tide for-ev-er Flow-ing by the throne of God?
We will walk and wor-ship ev-er, All the hap-py, gold-en day.
Grace our spir-its will de-liv-er, And pro-vide a robe and crown.
Soon our hap-py hearts will quiv-er, With the mel-o-dy of peace.

CHORUS

Yes, we'll gath-er at the riv-er, The beau-ti-ful, the beau-ti-ful riv-er,

Gath-er with the saints at the riv-er, That flows by the throne of God.

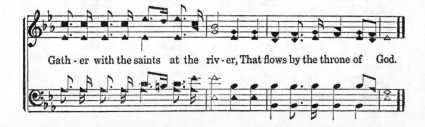

No. 214   If We Never Meet Again

A. E. B.   Albert E. Brumley

Slow

1. Soon we'll come to the end of life's jour-ney And per-haps we'll nev-er meet an-y more, Till we gath-er in heav-en's bright cit-y Far a-way on that beau-ti-ful shore.

2. O so oft-en we're part-ed with sor-row, Ben-e-dic-tions oft-en quick-en our pain, But we nev-er shall sor-row in heav-en, God be with you till we meet a-gain.

3. O they say we shall meet by the riv-er, Where no storm-clouds ev-er dark-en the sky, And they say we'll be hap-py in heav-en In the won-der-ful sweet by and by.

Chorus

Nev-er meet this side of heav-en
If we nev-er meet a-gain this side of heav-en

Strug-gle thru this world and its strife,
As we strug-gle thru this world and its strife, There's an-

If We Never Meet Again

Meet - ing place somewhere in heav - en
oth - er meet-ing place some-where in heav - en By the

By the shin - ing riv - er of life; Ros - es bloom
side of the riv - er of life; Where the charm - ing ros - es bloom for-

ev - er and ev - er, Sep - a - ra - tions
ev - er, And where sep - a - ra - tions come no

come nev - er more Nev - er meet
more, If we nev - er meet a - gain this side of

this side of heav-en Meet you on that beau-ti - ful shore.
heav-en I will meet you on that beau-ti - ful shore.

No. 215 I'll Meet You In The Morning

Respectfully dedicated to my wife, Goldie, and sons, Billey Joe, Albert E. Jr., Thomas Rexton,
Robert Bartlett, and Jackie Stamps.—A. E. B.

A. E. B.   Copyright, 1936, by Hartford Music Co., in "Lights of Life"   Albert E. Brumley

1. I will meet you in the morn-ing, by the bright riv-er side,
2. I will meet you in the morn-ing, in the sweet by and by,
3. I will meet you in the morn-ing, at the end of the way,

When all sor-row has drift-ed a-way; I'll be stand-ing at the
And ex-change the old cross for a crown; There will be no dis-ap-
On the streets of that cit-y of gold; Where we all can be to-

por-tals, when the gates o-pen wide, At the close of life's long, drear-y day.
point-ments and no-bod-y shall die, In that land where the sun go-eth down.
geth-er and be hap-py for aye, While the years and the a-ges shall roll.

Chorus

Meet you in the morn-ing,   meet you in the morn-ing,
I'll meet   you in the morn-ing,

"How do you do,"   "How do you do,"
with a "How   do you do,"   and we'll

I'll Meet You In The Morning

sit down by the riv - er,   sit down by the riv - er,
sit down   by the riv - er   and with

Rap - ture   our "auld" ac - quaint - ance re - new; Know me in the morn -
rap - ture "auld" ac - quaint - ance re - new;   You'll know

ing   know me in the morn - ing,   Smiles that I wear,
me in the morn - ing,   By the smiles   that I

smiles that I wear,   Meet you in the morn - ing,   meet you in the morn - ing,
wear,   When I meet you   in the morn - ing,

Cit - y,   cit - y built, that cit - y built four square.
In the cit - y that is built,   four square.

No. 216 In The Sweet Forever

L. G. P.

Luther G. Presley

1. What a hap-py time some glad tomorrow when we lay these heavy burdens down,
2. Nev-er-more the soul will be re - pining when we reach that happy resting place
3. Man-y precious loved ones will be wait-ing just a-cross the riv-er deep and wide,

In this lonesome val - ley   no more to roam;

In this lonesome vale   no more to roam;

Having labored on thru joy and sor-row hoping to re-ceive the golden crown,
Yonder where the sun is al-ways shin-ing we shall look up - on His smiling face,
Thru e - ter - ni - ty no sep - a - rat-ing, ev -'ry heart will then be sat - is - fied,

It will all be glo-ry   It will all be joy in that sweet home.

that hap - py home.

Chorus

In that beau-ti-ful ci - ty   Beau-ti-tul ci - ty   some hap-py day,

of the sweet for-ev - er

In The Sweet Forever

Where the riv-er of life goes ebbing by;
Where the riv-er of life goes ebbing by;

Look up-on the beauty fades not a-way,
We'll look upon the beau-ty that fades no nev-er,

And hap-py we'll be while the a - ges fly.
And happy we'll be while the a - ges fly.

No. 217   Blest Be the Tie

John Fawcett   Hans G. Nageli

1. Blest be the tie that binds Our hearts in Chris - tian love;
2. Be - fore our Fa - ther's throne, We pour our ar - dent pray'rs;
3. We share our mu - tual woes, Our mu - tual bur - dens bear;
4. When we a - sun - der part, It gives us in - ward pain;

The fel - low-ship of kin - dred minds Is like to that a - bove.
Our fears, our hopes, our aims are one, Our com - forts and our cares.
And oft - en for each oth - er flows The sym - pa - thiz - ing tear.
But we shall still be joined in heart, And hope to meet a - gain.

No. 218 Death Is Only A Dream

Rev. C. W. Ray

Music and Chorus by A. J. Buchanan

Effective as a solo

1. Sad - ly we sing and with trem - u - lous breath, As we stand by the
2. Why should we weep when the wea - ry ones rest, In the bos - om of
3. Naught in the riv - er the saints should ap - pall, Tho it fright-ful - ly
4. O - ver the tur - bid and on - rush-ing tide Doth the light of e -

mys - ti - cal stream, In the val - ley and by the dark
Je - sus su - preme, In the man - sions of glo - ry pre -
dis - mal may seem, In the arms of their Sav - ior no
ter - ni - ty gleam, And the ran-somed the dark - ness and

riv - er of death, And yet 'tis no more than a dream.
pared for the blest? For death is no more than a dream.
ill can be - fall, They find it no more than a dream.
storm shall out - ride, To wake with glad smiles from their dream.

CHORUS

On - ly a dream, on - ly a dream Of glo - ry be-yond the dark stream, How

peace-ful the slum-ber, how hap-py the wak-ing, For death is on - ly a dream.

No. 219 The Unclouded Day

Words & Melody by
Rev. J. K. Alwood

Arr. by J. K. A.

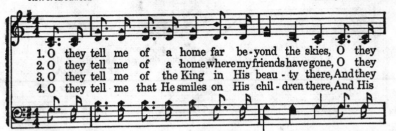

1. O they tell me of a home far be-yond the skies, O they
2. O they tell me of a home where my friends have gone, O they
3. O they tell me of the King in His beau-ty there, And they
4. O they tell me that He smiles on His chil-dren there, And His

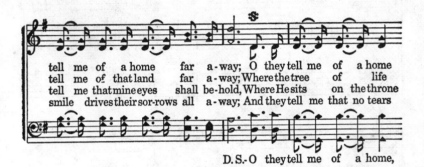

tell me of a home far a-way; O they tell me of a home
tell me of that land far a-way; Where the tree of life
tell me that mine eyes shall be-hold, Where He sits on the throne
smile drives their sor-rows all a-way; And they tell me that no tears

D.S.-O they tell me of a home,

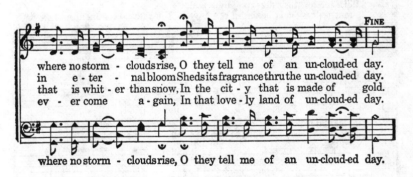

where no storm - clouds rise, O they tell me of an un-cloud-ed day.
in e - ter - nal bloom Sheds its fragrance thru the un-cloud-ed day.
that is whit - er than snow, In the cit - y that is made of gold.
ev - er come a - gain, In that love - ly land of un-cloud-ed day.

where no storm - clouds rise, O they tell me of an un-cloud-ed day.

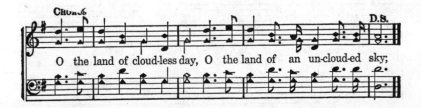

CHORUS

O the land of cloud-less day, O the land of an un-cloud-ed sky;

No. 220   I'd Rather Have Jesus

L. G. P.   Luther G. Presley

1. Men strive for the wealth of this wide, wick-ed world, They seek af - ter hon-
2. They seem not to know that their treasures will rust And thieves oft - en break
3. What prof - it is found in earth's sil - ver and gold? How sad at the close

or and fame; (worldly fame;) So lav - ish - ly sporting their diamonds and pearls,
thru and steal; (oft-en steal;) Con-tent - ed with pleasure, they fol-low their lust,
of life's day, (fleeting day,) If for the exchange one must lose his own soul,

Chorus

They put the dear Sav-ior to shame.   I'd rath-er live
With sor-row their des-ti - ny seal.
From heaven's door be turned a - way.   I'd rath - - er live in

in that bright ci - ty,   Own   earth's   sil-ver and gold,   I'd
heav - - en   Than to own all earth's sil-ver and gold,

I'd rath-er have   Je - sus my Sav - ior   Than   a
rath - - er have Je - - sus Than the diamonds of a pal-

I'd Rather Have Jesus

pal-ace to hold; I'd rath-er be just a poor beg-gar,
ace to hold;........ I'd rath - - er be a beg - - gar, Live

Live in a shack by the road, Than here to own
in a lit-tle shack by the road,........ Than to own........ all earth's

all of earth's treasures, With no ti-tle to a fu-ture a-bode.
treas - ures, to a fu-ture a-bode..........

No. 221 Must Jesus Bear The Cross Alone?

Thos. Shepherd   MAITLAND. C. M.   Geo. N. Allen

1. Must Je-sus bear the cross a-lone, And all the world go free?
2. The con-se-crat-ed cross I'll bear Till death shall set me free,
3. Up-on the crys-tal pave-ment, down At Je-sus' pierc-ed feet,
4. O pre-cious cross! O glo-rious crown! O res-ur-rec-tion day!

No, there's a cross for ev-'ry one, And there's a cross for me.
And then go home my crown to wear, For there's a crown for me.
Joy-ful, I'll cast my gold-en crown, And His dear name re-peat.
Ye an-gels from the stars come down, And bear my soul a-way.

I'll Meet You By The River

By the bright and shining riv-er
Bright and shin-ing riv-er so far a-way;
far a-way;

Af-ter we have flown these pris-on bars to a ci-ty far be-yond the stars,

I'll meet you by the riv-er
Meet you by the riv-er some sweet day.
some hap-py day.

No. 223 Ortonville

John Newton

Dr. Thomas Hastings

1. How sweet the name of Je-sus sounds, In a be-liev-er's ear! It soothes his
2. It makes the wounded spir-it whole, And calms the trou-bled breast; 'Tis man-na
3. By Him my pray'rs acceptance gain, Al-tho with sin de-filed, Sa-tan ac-

sorrows, heals his wounds, And drives a-way his fear, And drives away his fear.
to the hun-gry soul, And to the wea-ry rest, And to the wea-ry rest.
cus-es me in vain, And I am owned a child, And I am owned a child.

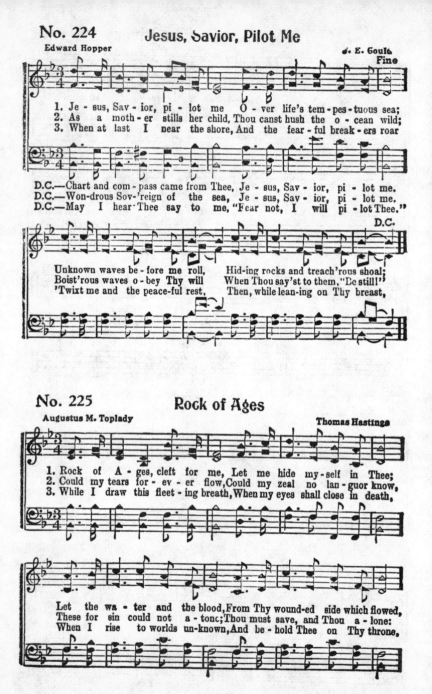

No. 224

Jesus, Savior, Pilot Me

Edward Hopper

J. E. Gould

Fine

1. Je - sus, Sav - ior, pi - lot me O - ver life's tem - pes - tuous sea;
2. As a moth - er stills her child, Thou canst hush the o - cean wild;
3. When at last I near the shore, And the fear - ful break - ers roar

D.C.—Chart and com - pass came from Thee, Je - sus, Sav - ior, pi - lot me.
D.C.—Won-drous Sov - 'reign of the sea, Je - sus, Sav - ior, pi - lot me.
D.C.—May I hear Thee say to me, "Fear not, I will pi - lot Thee."

D.C.

Unknown waves be - fore me roll, Hid-ing rocks and treach'rous shoal;
Boist'rous waves o - bey Thy will When Thou say'st to them, "Be still!"
'Twixt me and the peace-ful rest, Then, while lean-ing on Thy breast,

No. 225

Rock of Ages

Augustus M. Toplady

Thomas Hastings

1. Rock of A - ges, cleft for me, Let me hide my - self in Thee;
2. Could my tears for - ev - er flow, Could my zeal no lan - guor know,
3. While I draw this fleet - ing breath, When my eyes shall close in death,

Let the wa - ter and the blood, From Thy wound-ed side which flowed,
These for sin could not a - tone; Thou must save, and Thou a - lone:
When I rise to worlds un - known, And be - hold Thee on Thy throne,

Rock of Ages

Be of sin the dou-ble cure, Save from wrath and make me pure.
In my hand no price I bring, Sim-ply to Thy cross I cling.
Rock of A-ges, cleft for me, Let me hide my-self in Thee.

No. 226 Abide With Me

H. F. Lyte

W. H. Monk

1. A-bide with me: fast falls the e-ven-tide; The dark-ness
2. Swift to its close ebbs out life's lit-tle day; Earth's joys grow
3. I need Thy pres-ence ev-'ry pass-ing hour: What but Thy
4. Hold Thou Thy cross be-fore my clos-ing eyes; Shine thru the

deep-ens; Lord, with me a-bide: When oth-er help-ers fail, and
dim, its glo-ries pass a-way; Change and de-cay in' all a-
grace can foil the tempter's pow'r? Who like Thy-self my guide and
gloom, and point me to the skies; Heav'n's morning breaks, and earth's vain

com-forts flee, Help of the help-less, O a-bide with me!
round I see: O Thou who chang-est not, a-bide with me!
stay can be? Thru cloud and sun-shine, O a-bide with me!
shad-ows flee— In life, in death, O Lord, a-bide with me!

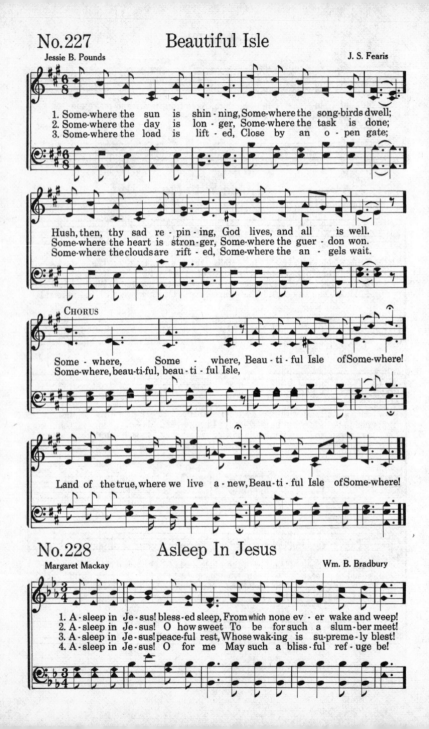

No. 227 Beautiful Isle

Jessie B. Pounds
J. S. Fearis

1. Some-where the sun is shin-ning, Some-where the song-birds dwell;
2. Some-where the day is lon-ger, Some-where the task is done;
3. Some-where the load is lift-ed, Close by an o-pen gate;

Hush, then, thy sad re-pin-ing, God lives, and all is well.
Some-where the heart is stron-ger, Some-where the guer-don won.
Some-where the clouds are rift-ed, Some-where the an-gels wait.

CHORUS

Some-where, Some-where, Beau-ti-ful Isle of Some-where!
Some-where, beau-ti-ful, beau-ti-ful Isle,

Land of the true, where we live a-new, Beau-ti-ful Isle of Some-where!

No. 228 Asleep In Jesus

Margaret Mackay
Wm. B. Bradbury

1. A-sleep in Je-sus! bless-ed sleep, From which none ev-er wake and weep!
2. A-sleep in Je-sus! O how sweet To be for such a slum-ber meet!
3. A-sleep in Je-sus! peace-ful rest, Whose wak-ing is su-preme-ly blest!
4. A-sleep in Je-sus! O for me May such a bliss-ful ref-uge be!

Asleep In Jesus

A calm and un-dis-turbed re-pose, Un-bro-ken by the last of foes.
With ho-ly con-fi-dence to sing, That death has lost his ven-omed sting.
No fear, no woe, shall dim that hour That man-i-fests the Sav-ior's pow'r.
Se-cure-ly shall my ash-es lie, Wait-ing the sum-mons from on high.

No. 229   We'll Never Say, Good-By

Mrs. E. W. Chapman

J. H. Tenney

1. With friends on earth we meet in glad-ness, While swift the mo-ments fly,
2. How joy-ful is the hope that lin-gers, When saved ones cross death's sea,
3. No part-ing words shall e'er be spok-en In yon-der home so fair,

Yea ev-er comes the tho't of sad-ness, That we must say good-by.
That we, when all earth's toils are end-ed, With them shall ev-er be.
But songs of joy, and peace, and glad-ness, We'll sing for-ev-er there.

CHORUS

We'll nev-er say good-by in heav'n, We'll nev-er say good-by;

good-by;

Repeat chorus *pp*

For in that land of joy and song, We'll nev-er say good-by.

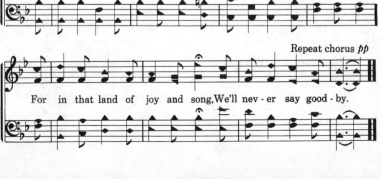

No. 230   The Pearly White City

Rev. 21:2
Copyright, 1929, by Arthur F. Ingle. Renewal
Lillenas Publishing Co., owner

A. F. I.

Arthur F. Ingle

Moderato

1. There's a ho - ly and beau-ti-ful ci - ty,   Whose builder and rul-er is God;
2. No   sin is allowed in that ci - ty,   And noth-ing de - fil-ing nor mean;
3. No   heartaches are known in that ci - ty,   No tears ev-er moisten the eye;
4. My   loved ones are gath-er-ing yon-der,   My friends, too, are passing a-way;

John saw it descending from heav-en,   When Patmos, in ex - ile, he trod;
No pain and no sickness can en - ter,   No crape on the door-knob is seen;
There's no disappointment in heav-en,   No en - vy and strife in the sky;
And soon I shall join their bright num-ber,   And dwell in e - ter - ni-ty's day;

Its high, massive wall is of jas-per,   The ci - ty it - self is pure gold;
Earth's sor-rows and cares are for-got-ten,   No tempt-er is there to an - noy;
The saints are all sanc-ti-fied whol-ly,   They live in sweet har-mo-ny there;
They're safe now in glo - ry with Je-sus,   Their tri-als and bat-tles are past;

Rit. ad libitum.

And when my frail tent here is fold-ed,   Mine eyes shall its glo - ry be - hold.
No part-ing words ev - er are spok-en,   There's nothing to hurt and de-stroy.
My heart is not set on that ci - ty,   And some day its bless-ing I'll share.
They o - ver-came sin and the tempter,   They've reached that fair ci - ty at last.

The Pearly White City

CHORUS *Slow*

It that bright ci-ty, pearly white ci-ty, I have a mansion, a harp and a crown;

Rit. ad libitum.

Now I am watch-ing, wait-ing and long-ing, For the white ci-ty that's soon com-ing down.

No. 231 Where The Roses Never Fade

E. J. & J.   Elsie, Jack & Jim

1. I am go-ing to a ci-ty Where the streets with gold are laid,
2. In this world we have our trou-bles, Sa-tan's snares we must e-vade;
3. Loved ones gone to be with Je-sus, In their robes of white ar-rayed,

FINE

Where the tree of life is bloom-ing, And the ros-es nev-er fade.
We'll be free from all temp-ta-tions Where the ros-es nev-er fade.
Now are wait-ing for my com-ing Where the ros-es nev-er fade.

D.S.—I am go-ing to a ci-ty Where the ros-es nev-er fade.

D.S.

CHORUS

Here they bloom but for a sea-son, Soon their beau-ty is de-cayed;

No. 232   Thou Art Gone

SAM. SHULTZ.

EMMETT S. DEAN.

1. Thou art gone,............ our precious dar-ling,............... Nev - er
2. Then be - yond............ this vale of sor - row,............... We'll a -
3. Thou art gone,............ our precious dar - ling, ... Nev - er
4. There we'll meet............ you, precious dar - ling, ... There we'll
5. There we'll spend............ the countless a - ges,............... Ev - er

1. Thou art gone, our precious darling, precious darling,

more......... canst thou re - turn;   Thou shalt sleep........ a peaceful
wake......... from ev - 'ry care;   In a cit - - y bright, e-
more......... we'll see thy face;   Till we meet........ thee o'er the
clasp.........glad hands once more;   When we've met,....... to part, no,
by.. .... our Saviour's side;   There we'll nev - - er know a

Never more canst thou return, canst thou return;   Thou shalt sleep a peaceful

slum - ber,...............   Till the res - - ur - rec - tion morn.
ter - nal,...............   And its joys .... we'll ev - er share.
riv - er,...............   In that hap - - py dwelling place.
nev - er,...............   On that hap - - py, peaceful shore.
sor - row,...............   There our tears............... will all be dried.

slumber, peaceful slumber,   Till the res - ur - rec - tion morn.

CHORUS.

We shall meet............... to part, no, nev - er,............... ....
We shall meet, to part, no, nev - er, part, no, nev - er,

Thou Art Gone

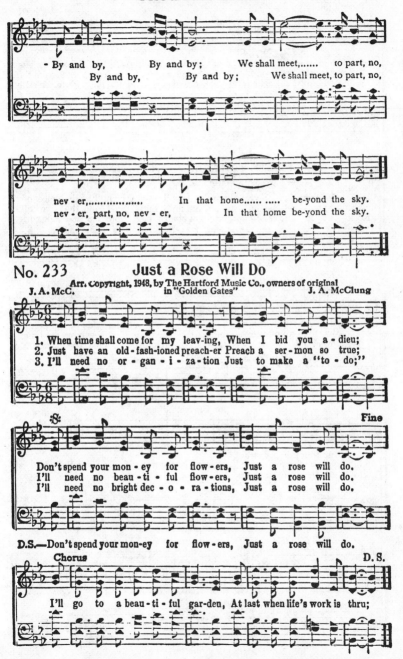

By and by, By and by; We shall meet,...... to part, no,
By and by, By and by; We shall meet, to part, no,

nev - er,.................. In that home...... ..... be-yond the sky.
nev - er, part, no, nev - er, In that home be-yond the sky.

No. 233 — **Just a Rose Will Do**

Arr. Copyright, 1948, by The Hartford Music Co., owners of original
in "Golden Gates"

J. A. McC.   J. A. McClung

1. When time shall come for my leav-ing, When I bid you a - dieu;
2. Just have an old - fash-ioned preach-er Preach a ser-mon so true;
3. I'll need no or - gan - i - za-tion Just to make a "to - do;"

Fine

Don't spend your mon - ey for flow - ers, Just a rose will do.
I'll need no beau-ti - ful flow - ers, Just a rose will do.
I'll need no bright dec - o - ra-tions, Just a rose will do.

D.S.—Don't spend your mon-ey for flow - ers, Just a rose will do.

Chorus   D. S.

I'll go to a beau-ti - ful gar-den, At last when life's work is thru;

No. 234 Safe In The Arms Of Jesus

Fanny J. Crosby

W. H. Doane

1. Safe in the arms of Je - sus, Safe on His gen - tle breast, There by His
2. Safe in the arms of Je - sus, Safe from cor - rod - ing care, Safe from the
3. Je - sus, my heart's dear ref - uge, Je-sus has died for me; Firm on the

love o'er-shad - ed, Sweet - ly my soul shall rest. Hark! 'tis the voice of
world's temp - ta-tions Sin can-not harm me there. Free from the blight of
Rock of A - ges, Ev - er my trust shall be. Here let me wait with

an - gels, Borne in a song to me, O - ver the fields of glo - ry,
sor - row, Free from my doubts and fears; On - ly a few more tri - als,
pa-tience, Wait till the night is o'er; Wait till I see the morn - ing

Chorus

O - ver the jas - per sea.
On - ly a few more tears! Safe in the arms of Je - sus, Safe on His
Break on the gold-en shore.

gen-tle breast, There by His love o'er-shad - ed, Sweet - ly my soul shall rest.

The City of Gold

And the city was pure gold, like unto clear glass. Rev. 21: 18

Adger M. Pace Copyright, 1929, by W. Z. Kitts W. Z. Kitts

1. In the Bi-ble we read of a cit-y Where the faith-ful shall
2. On the Is-land of Pat-mos John saw it, In its grand-eur he
3. O they need not the sun in that cit-y, For the glo-ry of
4. I ex-pect to live there in that cit-y While the years of e-

nev-er grow old; I have heard that its won-der-ful road-ways Are
saw it un-fold; And he saw that its walls were of jas-per, This
God, we are told, Is the light of that won-der-ful cit-y, The
ter-ni-ty roll; I ex-pect to live there with my Sav-ior In the

Chorus

1.v. built of the pur-est of gold. I long for that
234v.beau-ti-ful cit-y of gold. for that cit-y,

cit-y, Its walls are of jas-per I'm told; I'm
so rare, I am told;

bound for that cit-y, That beau-ti-ful cit-y of gold.
for that cit-y, so fair,

No. 236   We are Going Down the Valley

Jessie H. Brown

J. H. Fillmore

1. We are go-ing down the val-ley one by one, With our faces tow'rd the
2. We are go-ing down the val-ley one by one, When the la-bors of the
3. We are go-ing down the val-ley one by one, Hu-man comrade you or

set - ting of the sun; Down the valley where the mournful cypress grows, Where the
wea - ry day are done; One by one, the cares of earth for-ev - er past, We shall
I will there have none, But a ten-der hand will guide us lest we fall, Christ is

Chorus

stream of death in si - lence onward flows.
stand up - on the riv - er bank at last.   We are go - ing down the val-ley,
go - ing down the val - ley with us all.

go-ing down the valley,   Going tow'rd the setting of the sun; We are go-ing

down the valley,   go-ing down the valley,   Going down the valley one by one.

No. 237 When They Ring The Golden Bells

Dion De Marbelle

1. There's a land be-yond the riv-er, that we call the sweet for-ev-er, And we
2. We shall know no sin nor sor-row, in that hav-en of to-mor-row, When our
3. When our days shall know their num-ber, When in death we sweet-ly slum-ber, When the

on - ly reach that shore by faith's de-cree; One by one we'll gain the por-tals, there to
barque shall sail be-yond the sil-ver sea; We shall on-ly know the bless-ing of our
King com-mands the spir-it to be free; Nev-er-more with an-guish lad-en, we shall

dwell with the im-mor-tals, When they ring the gold-en bells for you and me.
Fa-ther's sweet ca-ress-ing,
reach that love-ly ai-den,   you and me.

D.S.-yond the shin-ing riv-er,

Chorus

Don't you hear the bells now ring-ing? don't you hear the an-gels sing-ing? 'Tis the

glo-ry hal-le-lu-jah Ju-bi-lee,   In that far-off sweet for-ev-er, just be-
Ju-bi-lee,

No. 238 God Be With You

J. E. Rankin, D. D.
W. G. Tomer

1. God be with you till we meet a-gain, By His coun-sels
2. God be with you till we meet a-gain, 'Neath His wings se-
3. God be with you till we meet a-gain, When life's per - ils
4. God be with you till we meet a-gain, Keep love's ban - ner

guide, up-hold you, With His sheep se - cure-ly fold you, God be
cure-ly hide you, Dai - ly man-na still pro-vide you, God be
thick confound you, Put His arms un - fail - ing round you, God be
float-ing o'er you, Smite death's threat'ning wave be-fore you, God be

CHORUS

with you till we meet a-gain. Till we meet, till we
Till we meet, till we

meet, Till we meet at Je - sus' feet, Till we
meet a - gain, till we meet,

meet, till we meet, God be with you till we meet a-gain.
Till we meet, till we meet a-gain,

No. 239
R. L.

Christ Arose!

Robert Lowery

1. Low in the grave He lay, Je-sus, my Sav-ior! Wait-ing the com-ing day,
2. Vain - ly they watch His bed, Je-sus, my Sav-ior! Vain - ly they seal the dead.
3. Death can-not keep his prey, Je-sus, my Sav-ior! He tore the bars a - way,

CHORUS

Je-sus my Lord! Up from the grave He a-rose! With a might-y
He a-rose!

tri-umph o'er His foes; He a-rose a vic-tor from the
He a-rose!

dark do-main, And He lives for-ev-er with His saints to reign, He a-

rit.

rose! He a-rose! Hal - le - lu - jah! Christ a-rose!
He a-rose! He a-rose!

No. 240 Hallelujah! We Shall Rise

"But if there be no resurrection of the dead, then is Christ not risen."--1 Cor. 15:12

J. E. T.

Copyright, 1932, by J. E. Thomas, renewal

J. E. Thomas

1. In the res-ur-rec-tion morning, When the trump of God shall sound,
2. In the res-ur-rec-tion morning, What a meet-ing it will be,
3. In the res-ur-rec-tion morning, Bless-ed tho't it is to me,
4. In the res-ur-rec-tion morning, We shall meet Him in the air,

We shall rise, we shall rise! Then the saints will come re-joic-ing,
Hal-le-lu-jah! When our fa-thers and our mothers,
I shall see my bless-ed Sav-ior,
And be car-ried up to glo-ry,

And no tears will e'er be found, We shall rise, we shall rise.
And our loved ones we shall see,
Who so free-ly died for me,
To our home so bright and fair, Hal-le-lu-jah! in that morning we shall rise.

CHORUS

We shall rise! Hal-le-lu-jah! we shall rise! A-men! We shall rise! Hal-le-lu-jah!

D. S.

In the res-ur-rec-tion morning, When death's prison bars are broken,

Lord, Build Me a Cabin In Glory

Cpl. Curtis Stewart

1. Man - y years I've been looking for a place to call home, But I've failed here to
2. Bless-ed Lord, I'm not ask-ing to live in the midst, For I know I'm not
3. I have man-y dear loved ones who have gone on this way, On that great fi - nal

find it, so I must trav - el on; I don't care for fine man-sions
wor-thy of such splen-dor as this, But I'm ask-ing for mer - cy
morn-ing, shall I hear them all say, Come and join in our sing - ing

FINE

on earth's sinking sand,
while humbly I stand, Lord, build me a cab-in in the cor-ner of glo - ry land.
and play in our band?

D.S. and shake Je-sus' hand;

CHORUS

Yes, build me just a cab-in in the cor-ner of glo - ry land, In the shade of the

D. S.

tree of life that it may ev-er stand; Where I can just hear the an - gels sing,

No. 242 When They Ring the Bells of Heaven

Albert E. Brumley & M. W. E.   Marion W. Easterling

1. That will be a hap-py morn-ing o - ver the sea,
2. Ev - er-last-ing glo - ry and an un - end-ing song,
3. Press a -long, re - joic-ing, thru this un-friend-ly land,

When the cares of life shall pass a -way; (shall pass a - way for - ev - er;)
With our great Re-deem-er we shall stay; (with Him we'll stay for-ev - er;)
Glo - ry land is wait-ing o'er the way; (the sun is al -ways shin-ing;)

Mu - sic there to wel-come all the ran-somed and free,
We shall join our loved ones in that heav-en - ly throng,
That will be a glad home-com-ing, won't it be grand, When they shall

Ring the bells of heav-en on that day.   O hal - le - lu -jah, when they

Chorus

Ring the bells of heav- en,   ring the bells of glo - ry,
heav- en,   glo - ry,

When They Ring The Bells of Heaven

When re-deemed are gathered home for aye;

on that hal - le - lu - jah morning;

Ev - 'ry bod - y sing- ing,   what a hap-py meet- ing,
shout- ing,
When they

Ring the bells of heav-en on that day.
that hap-py day.

No. 243   In His Care

1. Tho the cross be press-ing deep - ly We shall not de - spair,
2. Meet-ing rays of hope out-reach-ing Thru dark gath'ring clouds,
3. Emp- ty tomb, O glo -rious morning, Love has cleared the way,

With the Ho - ly One up - lift - ed, In our Fa -ther's care.
Look- ing up the light's ap-par- ent, Dawn a shad - ow shrouds,
We shall wear a crown im -mor- tal On that hap - py day.

No. 244　Like The Rainbow

J. R. Baxter, Jr.　　　　　　　　　　　　　　　　　Virgil O. Stamps

1. If you would make the world brighter As o'er life's pathway you tread,
2. If you would help bear the bur-dens Of the tired pilgrims be-low,
3. If you want friends here to miss you When you cross o-ver the tide,

If you would drive a-way sor-row, Hap-pi-ness 'round you spread;
If you would ban-ish their heart-aches, Make their path brightly glow;
If you want foot-prints be-hind you Safe-ly their feet to guide;

You must be faithful and earn-est, Look to the Sav-ior di-vine,
You must be read-y to help them See thru each e-vil de-sign,
You must be careful, my broth-er, Lest you should waste precious time,

You must be true in all you do, Just like the rain-bow shine.
Show them the way, teach them to pray, Just like the rain-bow shine.
Do-ing your best, un-der each test, Just like the rain-bow shine.

Chorus

Troubles,..... bur-dens, ...   cheer those who pine;
Troubles to share, bur-dens to bear, Help cheer the souls who pine:... .....

Like the Rainbow

Tell-ing,...... look-ing,...... let your light shine.

Tell-ing of love, look-ing a-bove, Just like the rain-bow shine..........

In Gethsemane Alone

S. B. R.   S. B. Reed.

1. Oh, what won-drous love I see Free-ly shown for you and me,
2. "Tar-ry here," He told the three, "Tar-ry here and watch with Me;"
3. Long in an-guish deep was He, Weep-ing there for you and me,

By the One who did a-tone! Pros-trate on His sa-cred face,
But they heard no bit-ter moan, For the three dis-ci-ples slept
For our sin to Him was known. We should love Him ev-er-more

D. S.—*His for-ev-er I will be,*

rit.   Fine.

Je-sus suf-fered for the race, In Geth-sem-a-ne, a-lone.
While my lov-ing Sav-ior wept In Geth-sem-a-ne, a-lone.
For the an-guish that He bore In Geth-sem-a-ne, a-lone.

For the love He gave to me, When He suf-fered all a-lone.

REFRAIN.   D. S

Oh, what love, match-less love, Oh, what love.... for me was shown!
Oh, what love, match-less love, Oh, what love for me was shown!

No. 246 My Sins Are Gone

N. B. V.   N. B. Vandall

1. You ask why I am hap-py so I'll just tell you why, Be-cause
2. 'Twas at the old time al-tar where God came in my heart And now,
3. When Sa-tan comes to tempt me and tries to make me doubt, I say,
4. I'm liv-ing now for Je-sus, I'm hap-py night and day, Be-cause

my sins are gone; And when I meet the scof-fers who ask me where they
my sins are gone; The Lord took full po-ses-sion, the dev-il did de-
my sins are gone; You got me in-to trou-ble, but Je-sus got me
my sins are gone; My soul is filled with mu-sic, with all my heart I

Chorus

are, I say, my sins are gone.
part, I'm glad my sins are gone. They're un-der-neath the Blood, on the
out, I'm glad my sins are gone.
say, I know my sins are gone.

Cross of Cal-va-ry, As far re-moved as dark-ness is from dawn; In the

Rit.

sea of God's forgetfulness, that's good enough for me, Praise God, my sins are gone.

No. 247 — Don't Forget Jesus

Miss Lessie Reddell   R. J. Weaver

1. When you are wea-ry and by sin op-pressed, Trust in the Sav-ior,
2. Tho' you are sad and ev-'ry-thing seems blue, Don't forget Je-sus
3. If you are drift-ing, tossed a-bout by sin, Don't for-get Je-sus

He can give you rest; He will be with you by night and by day,
for He tho't of you; Pray to the Sav-ior, a new life be-gin,
will help you to win; He is your Sav-ior and on Him re-ly,

CHORUS

Don't for-get Je-sus will hear when you pray.
Je-sus will hear you and save you from sin. Don't for-get Je-sus, the
Some day you'll need Him, the time draweth nigh.

Man of Gal-li-lee, He is so lov-ing, so kind and so true; Don't forget

Je-sus who died on Cal-va-ry, For Je-sus remembered you........
re-membered you.

No. 248   It Took a Miracle

J. W. P.

John W. Peterson

1. My Father is om-ni-po-tent, And that you can't de-ny,
2. Though here His glo-ry has been shown; We still can't ful-ly see
3. The Bi-ble tells us of His pow'r And wis-dom all way through;

A God of might and mir-a-cles 'Tis writ-ten in the sky.
The won-ders of His might, His throne; 'Twill take e-ter-ni-ty.
And ev-'ry lit-tle bird and flow'r Are tes-ti-mo-nies, too.

Chorus

It took a mir-a-cle to put the stars in place. It took a mir-a-cle to hang the world in space. But when He saved my soul, cleansed and made me whole, It took a mir-a-cle of love and grace.

No. 249 After The Sunrise

J. R. Baxter, Jr. Sug. by E. W.   Eugene Wright

1. Sor-rows sur-round us while tread-ing life's road, Trou - bles con-found us, make
2. Shad-ows will van-ish when morn-ing shall come, Love - light will ban-ish sin's
3. An - gels are wait-ing to car - ry the news, Why stand de-bat-ing, why

heav-y our load; Fet-ters that bound us, no long-er will goad, Af-ter the
va-pors like scum; Ev - en the clan-ish to - geth-er will hum, Af-ter the
lon-ger re-fuse? Cease all your hat - ing, be chang-ing your views, Af-ter the

CHORUS

sun-rise, how hap-py we'll be. Af-ter the sun-rise, hap-py we'll be

We know af-ter the sun-rise, Je-sus we'll see; in heav-en; All will be

glo - ry, sing-ing the sto - ry, Af-ter the sun-rise, how hap-py we'll be.

No. 250   Send The Light

C. H. G.

Chas. H. Gabriel

1. There's a call comes ring-ing o'er the rest-less wave, Send the light!
2. We have heard the Ma-ce-don-ian call to-day,
3. We will pray that grace may ev-'ry-where a-bound,
4. We will not grow wea-ry in the work of love,   Send the light!

send the light!   There are souls to res-cue, there are
     And a gold-en of-f'ring at the
     And a Christ-like spir-it ev-'ry-
send the light! Let us gath-er jew-els for a

souls to save, Send the light!   send the light!
cross we lay,
where be found,
crown a-bove,   Send the light!   send the light!

CHORUS

Send the light! .... the bless-ed gos-pel light, Let it
Send the light! the bless-ed gos-pel light,

shine .... from shore to shore! .... for-ev-er-more. ....
Let it shine   from shore to shore!   for-ev-er-more.

No. 251 Stand Up, Stand Up For Jesus!

George Duffield, Jr.

George J. Webb

1. Stand up, stand up for Jesus! Ye sol-diers of the cross;
2. Stand up, stand up for Jesus! The trump-et call o-bey;
3. Stand up, stand up for Jesus! Stand in His strength a-lone;
4. Stand up, stand up for Jesus! The strife will not be long;

Lift high His roy-al ban-ner, It must not suf-fer loss:
Forth to the might-y con-flict, In this His glo-rious day;
The arm of flesh will fail you; Ye dare not trust your own;
This day the noise of bat-tle, The next the vic-tor's song:

From vic-t'ry un-to vic-t'ry His arm-y shall He lead,
Ye that are men, now serve Him, A-gainst un-num-bered foes;
Put on the gos-pel ar-mor, Each piece put on with pray'r;
To him that o-ver-com-eth, A crown of life shall be;

Till ev-'ry foe is van-quished And Christ is Lord in-deed.
Your cour-age rise with dan-ger, And strength to strength op-pose.
Where du-ty calls, or dan-ger, Be nev-er want-ing there.
He with the King of glo-ry Shall reign e-ter-nal-ly.

The Glory-land Way

J. S. T.

J. S. Torbett

1. I'm in the way, the bright and shin-ing way, I'm in the glo-ry-land
2. List to the call, the gos-pel call to-day, Get in the glo-ry-land
3. On-ward I go re-joic-ing in His love, I'm in the glo-ry-land

way;

glo-ry-land way;

Tell-ing the world that Je-sus saves to-day, Yes,
Wand'rers, come home, O hast-en to o-bey, For
Soon I shall see Him in that home a-bove, O

I'm in the glo-ry-land way.
glo-ry-land way.

CHORUS

I'm in the glo-ry-land

way,
glo-ry-land way,

I'm in the glo-ry-land way;
glo-ry-land way;

Heav-en is

near-er and the way grow-eth clear-er, For I'm in the glo-ry-land way.
glo-ry land way.

No. 253 That's Him

L. G. P.   in "Crimson Glow"   **Luther G. Presley**

1. If you meet a stran-ger on the Jer-i-cho road, That's Him, that's
2. If some-bod-y calls you in the still of the night,
3. If some-bod-y watch-es with a tear or a sigh, That's Him,

Him;   If He walks be-side you, free-ly shar-ing your load, That's
   If you feel a yearn-ing for a life that is right,
that's Him; If He says my child I need you, nev-er ask why?

Chorus

Him, that's Him. That's Him, my Sav-ior,
That's Him, that's Him. That's Him, don't you know,

This man of Gal-i-lee whose blood a-vails for me, If He fills
    If He fills

your cup to the brim, That's Him, that's Him.
    That's Him, that's Him.

No. 254 When He Blest My Soul

(SPIRITUAL)

C. D. and J. R. B.

Cleavant Derricks

1. Je - sus washed my sin a - way one glo - ri - ous morning,
2. Je - sus made my spir - it glad
3. Je - sus claimed me as His own

praise His dear name,

He blest my soul   and He made me whole;
He blest my soul   He made me whole;

Ev - er since that hap - py day I'm tell-ing the sto - ry,
Ev - er to the lone and sad
Ev - er since this joy I've known

praise His dear name,

How He washed my sin a - way when He blest my soul.

when He blest my soul.

Chorus

That blessed morning,   of the Lord came down,
Well, you oughta been there   when the love

When He Blest My Soul

In-to my soul and He made me whole; ....
In-to my soul .... and He made me whole;

You'd-a shouted glo-ry to my Lord and King,
If you'd-a been there, to the Lamb,

Yes, you ought-a been there when He blest my soul.........
Well, you ought-a been there .... when He blest my soul.

Hide Me In The Rock Of Ages

No. 255

Copyright, 1939, by Stamps-Baxter Music & Ptg. Co., in "Joyful Songs."
Renewed 1967. All Rights Reserved.

J. R. B., Jr.   J. R. Baxter, Jr.

O dear broth-er* when the world is burn-ing, Don't you want God's bos-om to

be your pil-low? Hide me in the Rock of A-ges, Rock of A-ges cleft for me.

* Sister, father, mother, sinner, mourner, etc., may be used for extra stanzas.

No. 256 Press Along to Glory-land

JAMES ROWE EMMETT S. DEAN

1. O ransomed souls, with joyous song, Press a-long to Glo-ry-land;
2. The foe may rave, but Christ will save,
3. To join once more those gone before,
4. The crown to wear for-ev-er there, Press along

Ex-tol-ling grace that saves the race, Press along to Glo-ry-land.
The storm may sweep, but He will keep,
With saints to sing be-fore the King,
To sing His praise thru countless days, Press a-long

Chorus

Press a-long, glad soul, press a-long, Giv-ing
Press a-long,

out the mes-sage grand; Let-ting love, God's
Giv-ing out Let-ting love,

love, be your song, Press a-long to Glo-ry-land.
Press a-long

No. 257 Sunlight

W. Van DeVenter

W. S. Weeden

1. I wan-dered in the shades of night, Till Je-sus came to me,
2. Tho' clouds may gath-er in the sky, And bil-lows round me roll,
3. While walk-ing in the light of God, I sweet com-mun-ion find;
4. I cross the wide ex-tend-ed fields, I jour-ney o'er the plain,
5. Soon I shall see Him as He is, The light that came to me,

And with the sun-light of His love Bid all my dark-ness flee.
How-ev-er dark the world may be, I've sun-light in my soul.
I press with ho-ly vig-or on, And leave the world be-hind.
And in the sun-light of His love I reap the gold-en grain.
Be-hold, the bright-ness of His face, Thro'-out e-ter-ni-ty.

Chorus

Sun-light, sun-light in my soul to-day,
to-day, yes,
Sun-light, sun-light

all a-long the way;
nar-row way;
Since the Sav-ior found me,

took a-way my sin,
load of sin,
I have had the sun-light of His love with-in.

No. 258 Since Jesus Came Into My Heart

R. H. McDaniel　　　　　　　　　　　　　　　　　Chas. H. Gabriel

1. What a won-der-ful change in my life has been wrought Since Je-sus came
2. I have ceased from my wand'ring and go-ing a-stray, Since Je-sus came
3. I'm pos-sessed of a hope that is stead-fast and sure, Since Je-sus came
4. There's a light in the val-ley of death now for me, Since Je-sus came
5. I shall go there to dwell in that Cit-y I know, Since Je-sus came

in-to my heart; I have light in my soul for which long I had sought
in-to my heart; And my sins which were man-y are all washed a-way,
in-to my heart; And no dark clouds of doubt now my path-way ob-scure,
in-to my heart; And the gates of the Cit-y be-yond I can see
in-to my heart; And I'm hap-py, so hap-py as on-ward I go,

CHORUS

Since Je-sus came in-to my heart. Since Je-sus came in-to my
　　　　　　　　　　　　　　　　　　Since Je-sus came in, came

heart, Since Je-sus came in-to my heart; Floods of joy o'er my
in-to my heart, Since Je-sus came in, came in-to my heart;

soul like the sea bil-lows roll, Since Je-sus came in-to my heart.

No. 259 That's Why I Love Him So

L. B. C.

Lonnie B. Combs

1. The path-way of sin so long I had trod, Till Je-sus came from a-
2. Tho friends in this land may turn me a-way, Yet Christ will my pray'rs at-
3. I'm hap-py to-day while go-ing a-long, The Sav-ior is kind and

bove, (from realms a-bove,) He spoke peace to me, O glo-ry to God, What
tend, (He will at-tend,) I'm glad in my heart that now I can say That
true; (so kind and true;) He lift-ed me up and gave me a song, I

CHORUS

mer-cy, what wondrous love. (what wondrous love.)
Je-sus is my best friend. (is my best friend.) O glo-ry to God, He's
sing it the whole day thru. (the whole day thru.)

hold-ing my hand He safe-ly will guide, I know; He lift-ed me
my soul, I know;

up and caused me to stand, O that's why I love Him so.

I love Him so.

No. 260 The Wayfaring Stranger

Words arr.

Arr. from an old Southern Melody

1. I am a poor way-far-ing stran-ger, While trav-'ling thro' this world be-low;
2. I know dark clouds will gath-er o'er me, I know my path - way's rough and steep;
3. I want to sing sal - va-tion's sto - ry In con-cert with the blood-washed band;
4. I'll soon be free from ev - ery tri - al, This form will rest be-neath the sod;

There is no sick-ness, toil, nor dan-ger In that bright world to which I go.
But gold - en fields lie out be-fore me, Where wea - ry eyes no more shall weep.
I want to wear a crown of glo - ry, When I get home to that good land.
I'll drop the cross of self - de - ni - al, And en - ter in my home with God.

I'm go-ing there to meet my fa-ther, I'm go - ing there no more to roam;
I'm go-ing there to see my moth-er, She said she'd meet me when I come;
I'm go-ing there to see my class-mates, Who passed be - fore me one by one;
I'm go-ing there to see my Sav-iour, Who shed for me His pre-cious blood;

I am just go - ing o - ver Jor - dan, I am just go - ing o - ver home.

No. 261 Will There Be Any Stars?

E. E. Hewitt

Jno. R. Sweney

1. I am think-ing to-day of that beau-ti-ful land I shall reach when the
2. In the strength of the Lord let me la-bor and pray, Let me watch as a
3. O what joy will it be when His face I be-hold, Liv-ing gems at His

sun go-eth down; When thro' won-der-ful grace by my Sav-ior I stand, Will there
win-ner of souls; That bright stars may be mine in the glo-ri-ous day, When His
feet to lay down; It would sweet-en my bliss in the cit-y of gold, Should there

CHORUS

be an-y stars in my crown?
praise like the sea-bil-lows roll Will there be an-y stars, an-y stars in my crown,
be an-y stars in my crown?

When at eve-ning the sun go-eth down? . . . . When I wake with the blest,
go-eth down?

In the man-sions of rest, Will there be an-y stars in my crown?
an-y stars in my crown?

No. 262 Tell Me The Old, Old Story

Kate Hankey

W. H. Doane

1. Tell me the old, old sto - ry Of un-seen things a - bove, Of Je - sus
2. Tell me the sto - ry slow - ly, That I may take it in— That won-der-
3. Tell me the sto - ry soft - ly, With earnest tones, and grave; Re-mem-ber,
4. Tell me the same old sto - ry, When you have cause to fear That this world's

and his glo - ry, Of Je - sus and his love. Tell me the sto - ry
ful re - demp-tion, God's rem-e - dy for sin. Tell me the sto - ry
I'm the sin - ner Whom Je - sus came to save. Tell me the sto - ry
emp - ty glo - ry, Is cost-ing me too dear; Yes, and when that world's

sim - ply, As to a lit - tle child, For I am weak and wea - ry, And
of - ten, For I for - get so soon; The "ear-ly dew" of morn-ing, Has
al - ways, If you would real - ly be, In a - ny time of trou - ble, A
glo - ry Is dawn - ing on my soul, Tell me the old, old sto - ry: "Christ

CHORUS

help - less and de - filed.
passed a - way at noon. Tell me the old, old sto - ry, Tell me the old, old
com - fort - er to me.
Je - sus makes thee whole."

sto - ry, Tell me the old, old sto - ry Of Je - sus and His love.

No. 263 The Haven Of Rest

H. L. Gilmour

Geo. D. Moore

1. My soul in sad ex - ile was out on life's sea, So bur-dened with
2. I yield - ed my-self to His ten-der em-brace, And faith tak - ing
3. The song of my soul, since the Lord made me whole, Has been the old
4. How pre-cious the tho't that we all may re - cline, Like John the be-
5. O come to the Sav - ior, He pa-tient - ly waits, To save by His

sin and dis-tressed, Till I heard a sweet voice say - ing, Make me your choice;
hold of the Word, My fet - ters fell off, and I an-chored my soul;
sto - ry so blest, Of Je - sus, who'll save who-so - ev - er will have
lov - ed and blest, On Je - sus' strong arm, where no tem-pest can harm,
pow - er di - vine; Come, an-chor your soul in the Ha - ven of Rest,

CHORUS

And I en - tered the Ha - ven of Rest.
The Ha - ven of Rest is my Lord.
A home in the Ha - ven of Rest.   I've an-chored my soul in the
Se - cure in the Ha - ven of Rest.
And say, My be - lov - ed is mine.

Ha - ven of rest, I'll sail the wide seas no more; The tem-pest may

sweep o'er the wild storm - y deep; In Je - sus I'm safe ev - er-more.

No. 264 The Keys to the Kingdom

J. L. C.

Jenny Lou Carson

1. You hold the keys to the king-dom of God, Use them now, friend, and
2. Don't lose your keys to the king-dom of God, For you can't buy your

when you be-gin, Start with the key that will un-lock your heart,
way to the fold, Lov-eth thy neigh - bor, for love is the key

O - pen up and let Je-sus come in; The mas-ter key's next, my dear
To that heaven - ly mansion of gold; When trumpets ring out in the

neigh-bor, It's one you should use ev-'ry day, Prayer is the
morn-ing, And you step where angels have trod, That's the great

key to the great pearly gates, Yes, you're unlock-ing them when you pray.
day, you'll be so glad you used All the keys to the kingdom of God.

No. 265 Shelter From The Storms

B. F.

Copyright 1946, by Byron Faust

Byron Faust

1. There are man-y storms that come a-long my pil-grim way, There are man-y things that would an-noy, that would an-noy; Save and keep me from all harm, dear Lord I hum-bly pray, Keep me from the things that would de-stroy, that would de-stroy.

2. Keep me calm when e-vil snares are thrown by fel-low men, May I take them as a chris-tian should, a chris-tian should; Tho' my heart he breaks and tears, by e-vil deeds of sin, Help me Lord, to o-ver-come with good, with deeds of good.

3. When I come to cross the tide at close of life's long day, And I set my sails for worlds un-known, for worlds un-known; Be my shel-ter and my Guide when storms are o'er my way, Bless-ed Sav-iour lead me safe-ly home, yes, leads me home.

D.S.-Un-der-neath Thy lov-ing arms, Lord, keep me safe each day, Hide me safe-ly in Thy love di-vine, Thy love di-vine.

FINE CHORUS

Give me shel-ter from the storms that come a-long my way, Let Thy sweet pro-tec-tion then be mine, for-ev-er mine;

D.S.

No. 266   Some Glad Day After While

W. M. R.

Will M. Ramsey
and Clyde Williams

1. O bless-ed tho't .... sweet rest will come, ... Some glad day
2. These heav-y loads .... we shall lay down,
3. Our suf-f'ring, too, ... will soon be past, ...
4. All war and strife .... will soon be o'er, ...
Some glad day

af-ter while;   When all our toil .... on earth is done, ...
When we re-ceive .... our heav'n-ly crown,
When we shall find ...... sweet rest at last, ...
af-ter while; We'll find sweet peace .... on heav-en's shore, ...

Chorus

Fine

There'll come a glad day   af-ter while.   O af-ter
af-ter while.

while,   af-ter while,   There'll come a glad day
Af-ter while,   af-ter while,

D.S.

af-ter while;   O af-ter while,   af-ter while,
af-ter while;   Af-ter while,   af-ter while,

No. 267   Saved By Grace

Geo. C. Stebbins
J. R. Baxter, Jr.

Fanny J. Crosby

1. Some day the sil-ver cord will break, And I no more as now shall sing;
2. Some day my earth-ly house will fall, I can-not tell how soon 'twill be;
3. Some day when fades the golden sun Beneath the ros-y tint-ed west,
4. Some day! till then I'll watch and wait, My lamp all trimmed and burning bright,

But, O the joy when I shall wake Within the pal-ace of the King!
But this I know, my All in All Has now a place in heav'n for me.
My bless-ed Lord shall say, "well done!" And I shall en-ter in-to rest.
That when my Sav-ior ope's the gate, My soul to Him may take its flight.

Chorus

And I shall see Him face to face, And tell the sto-ry, Saved by grace;
shall see   to face,

And I shall see Him face to face, And tell the story, Saved by grace.
shall see   to face,

No. 268 Only Through Grace

J. P. L.
J. P. Lane

Earnestly

1. On - ly thro' grace, O won-der-ful sto - ry! On - ly thro' grace, pro-
2. On - ly thro' grace our Fa-ther in heav-en Sent His dear Son to
3. On - ly thro' grace we press on our jour-ney, Kept by the pow'r of

long the sweet sound! On - ly thro' grace, it ech - oes in glo - ry!
die in our place; Life and sal - va - tion thro' Him are giv - en,
God till the end; On - ly thro' grace we'll en - ter the por-tals,

CHORUS

On - ly thro' grace, the lost has been found!
Won-der-ful love! O won-der-ful grace! Won-der-ful sto-ry! won-der-ful
Then to the Fa-ther grace will commend.

Sav - ior! Je - sus has died, and rose from the grave! Join the glad

cho-rus, praise Him for - ev - er, - Je - sus has died, lost sin-ners to save!

No. 269 — Sweet Hour Of Prayer

W. W. Walford

Wm. B. Bradbury

1. Sweet hour of prayer! sweet hour of prayer! That calls me from a world of care,
2. Sweet hour of prayer! sweet hour of prayer! Thy wings shall my pe - ti - tion bear
3. Sweet hour of prayer! sweet hour of prayer! May I thy con so - la - tion share

And bids me at my Fa-ther's throne Make all my wants and wish-es known;
To Him whose truth and faith-ful-ness En-gage the wait - ing soul to bless;
Till, from Mount Pis-gah's loft - y height, I view my home, and take my flight:

In sea - sons of dis - tress and grief, My soul has oft - en found re - lief,
And since He bids me seek His face, Be-lieve His word and trust His grace,
This robe of flesh I'll drop, and rise To seize the ev - er - last - ing prize,

And oft es-caped the tempt-er's snare By thy re-turn, sweet hour of prayer.
I'll cast on Him my ev - 'ry care, And wait for thee, sweet hour of prayer.
And shout, while pass-ing thru the air, Fare-well, fare-well, sweet hour of prayer.

No. 270 I Won't Have to Cross Jordan Alone

To my friend V. O. Stamps—C. E. D.

Copyright. 1934 by Stamps-Baxter Music Co. Assigned 1938 to Robert H. Coleman

Thomas Ramsey   Broadman Press Owner   Chas. E. Durham

May be used as a Solo

1. When I come to the riv-er at end-ing of day, When the last winds of
2. Oft-en-times I'm for-sak-en, and wea-ry and sad, When it seems that my
3. Tho the bil-lows of sor-row and trouble may sweep, Christ the Savior will

sor-row have blown;...... There'll be some-bod-y wait-ing to show me the
friends have all gone;...... There is one tho't that cheers me and makes my heart
care for His own;...... Till the end of the jour-ney, my soul He will

Chorus

way, I won't have to cross Jor-dan a-lone. I won't have to cross
glad, I won't have to cross Jor-dan a-lone.
keep, I won't have to cross Jor-dan a-lone. I won't have

Jor-dan a-lone,.......... Je-sus died all my sins to a-tone;
to cross Jor-dan a-lone,

Solo ad lib.   Parts

When the darkness I see, He'll be waiting for me, I won't have to cross Jordan alone.
Hum......   Hum......

No. 271 Joy To The World!

ANTIOCH

Isaac Watts

George F. Handel

1. Joy to the world! the Lord is come; Let earth re-
2. Joy to the earth! the Saviour reigns; Let men their
3. No more let sins and sorrows grow, Nor thorns in-
4. He rules the world with truth and grace, And makes the

ceive her King; Let ev-ery heart pre-pare Him room,
songs employ; While fields and floods, rocks, hills and plains
fest the ground, He comes to make His bless-ings flow
na-tions prove The glo-ries of His right-eous-ness,

And heaven and na-ture sing, And heaven and na-ture
Re-peat the sound-ing joy, Re-peat the sound-ing
Far as the curse is found, Far as the curse is
And won-ders of His love, And won-ders of His
1. And heaven and na-ture sing,.......... And

sing, And heaven, and heaven and na-ture sing.
joy, Re-peat, re-peat the sound-ing joy.
found, Far as, far as the curse is found.
love, And won-ders, and won-ders of His love.
heaven and na-ture sing,

The First Noel

Traditional
Traditional

1. The first No - el the an - gels did say Was to certain poor shep - herds in fields as they lay; In fields where they lay keep-ing their sheep, On a cold win-ters night that was so deep.

2. And by the light of that same Star, Three wise men came from coun - - try far; To seek for a King was their in - tent, And so fol - low the Star wher - ev - er it went.

3. This Star drew nigh to the north - west, O'er Beth - le - hem it took its rest; And there it did both stop and stay, Right o - ver the place where Je - sus lay.

4. Then en - tered in those wise men there, Full rev - 'rent - ly up - on their knee; And of - fered there in His pres - ence, Their gold, and myrrh and frank - in - cense.

CHORUS

No - el, No - el, No - el, No - el, Born is the King of Is - ra - el.

No. 273 We Three Kings Of Orient Are

John H. Hopkins | KINGS OF ORIENT | John H. Hopkins

1. We three kings of O - ri - ent are, Bear - ing gifts we trav-erse a - far
2. Born a King on Beth-le-hem's plain, Gold I bring to crown Him a - gain,
3. Frank-in-cense to of - fer have I, In-cense owns a De - i - ty nigh;
4. Myrrh is mine; its bit - ter per-fume Breathes a life of gath-er - ing gloom;
5. Glo-rious now be - hold Him a - rise, King and God and Sac - ri - fice;

Field and foun-tain, moor and moun - tain, Fol - low - ing yon - der star.
King for - ev - er, ceas - ing nev - er O - ver us all to reign.
Prayer and prais - ing, all men rais - ing, Wor - ship Him, God on high.
Sor - row, sigh - ing, bleed - ing, dy - ing, Sealed in the stone - cold tomb.
Al - le - lu - ia, Al - le - lu - ia! Peals through the earth and skies.

CHORUS

O star of won - der, star of night, Star with loy - al beau - ty bright,

West-ward lead - ing, still pro - ceed - ing, Guide us to Thy per - fect light.

No. 274   O LITTLE TOWN OF BETHLEHEM

Phillips Brooks

Lewis H. Redner

1. O lit - tle town of Beth - le-hem, How still we see thee lie!
2. For Christ is born of Ma - ry; And gath - ered all a - bove,
3. How si - lent - ly, how si - lent - ly The won - drous gift is giv'n!
4. O ho - ly Child of Beth - le-hem, De - scend to us, we pray;

A - bove thy deep and dream-less sleep The si - lent stars go by;
While mor-tals sleep the an - gels keep Their watch of wond'ring love.
So God im - parts to hu - man hearts The bless - ings of His heav'n.
Cast out our sin and en - ter in, Be born in us to - day.

Yet in thy dark streets shin - eth The ev - er - last - ing Light;
O morn - ing stars, to - geth - er Pro - claim the ho - ly birth,
Nor ear may hear His com - ing; But in this world of sin,
We hear the Christ-mas an - gels The great glad ti - dings tell,

The hopes and fears of all the years Are met in thee to - night.
And prais - es sing to God the King, And peace to men on earth.
Where meek souls will re - ceive Him still, The dear Christ en - ters in.
O come to us, a - bide with us, Our Lord Em - man - u - el.

It Came Upon the Midnight Clear.

E. H. Sears.   (Carol.)   R. Storrs Willis.

1. It came up-on the mid-night clear, That glo-rious song of old,
2. Still thro' the clo-ven skies they come With peace-ful wings un-furled,
3. Yet with the woes of sin and strife The world has suf-fered long;
4. For lo! the days are has-t'ning on, By proph-ets seen of old,

From an-gels bend-ing near the earth To touch their harps of gold:
And still their heav'n-ly mu-sic floats O'er all the wear-y world;
Be-neath the an-gel-strain have rolled Two thou-sand years of wrong;
When with the ev-er-cir-cling years, Shall come the time fore-told;

"Peace on the earth, good-will to men, From heav'n's all-gra-cious King."
A-bove its sad and low-ly plains They bend on hov-'ring wing,
And men, at war with men, hear not The love-song which they bring:
When the whole heav'n and earth shall own The Prince of Peace their King,

The world in sol-emn still-ness lay To hear the an-gels sing.
And ev-er, o'er its Ba-bel sounds, The bless-ed an-gels sing.
O hush the noise, ye men of strife, And hear the an-gels sing.
And the whole world send back the song Which now the an-gels sing.

No. 276 Hark, The Herald Angels Sing

MENDELSSOHN

Charles Wesley

Felix Mendelssohn

1. Hark! the her-ald an-gels sing, "Glo-ry to the new-born King;
2. Christ, by high-est heav'n a-dorn; Christ the ev-er-last-ing Lord;
3. Hail the heav'n-born Prince of Peace! Hail the Sun of right-eous-ness!
4. Come, De-sire of na-tions, come! Fix in us Thy hum-ble home:

Peace on earth, and mer-cy mild; God and sin-ners rec-on-ciled."
Late in time be-hold Him come, Off-spring of a vir-gin's womb.
Light and life to all He brings, Risen with heal-ing in His wings;
Rise, the wom-an's con-quering seed, Bruise in us the ser-pent's head;

Joy-ful, all ye na-tions, rise, Join the tri-umph of the skies,
Veiled in flesh the God-head see, Hail th'in-car-nate De-i-ty!
Mild He lays His glo-ry by, Born that man no more may die;
Ad-am's like-ness now ef-face, Stamp Thine im-age in its place;

With th'an-gel-ic hosts pro-claim, "Christ is born in Beth-le-hem."
Pleased as man with men t'ap-pear, Je-sus our Im-man-uel here.
Born to raise the sons of earth; Born to give them sec-ond birth.
Sec-ond Ad-am from a-bove, Re-in-state us in Thy love.

Hark, The Herald Angels Sing

Hark! the her-ald an-gels sing, "Glo-ry to the new-born King."

No. 277 O Come, All Ye Faithful

Tr. by Frederick Oakeley

Wade's Cantus Deversi

1. O come, all ye faith-ful, joy-ful and tri-um-phant, O
2. Sing, choirs of an-gels, sing in ex-ul-ta-tion, O
3. Yea, Lord, we greet Thee, born this hap-py morn-ing,

come ye, O come ye to Beth-le-hem; Come and be-hold Him
sing, all ye bright host of heaven a-bove; Glo-ry to God, all
Je-sus, to Thee be all glo-ry given; Word of the Fa-ther,

CHORUS

born the King of an-gels;
glo-ry in the high-est; O come, let us a-dore Him, O
now in flesh ap-pear-ing;

come, let us a-dore Him, O come, let us a-dore Him, Christ, the Lord.

No. 278   Silent Night, Holy Night

Joseph Mohr   Franz Gruber

1. {Si-lent night! / Ho-ly night!} All is calm, all is bright; {Round yon vir-gin moth-er and child, / Ho-ly In-fant so ten-der and mild,}

2. {Si-lent night! / Ho-ly night!} Shep-herds quake at the sight; {Glo-ries stream from heav-en a-far, / Heav-'nly host sing Al-le-lu-ia,}

3. {Si-lent night! / Ho-ly night!} Son of God, love's pure light; {Ra-diant beams from Thy ho-ly face / With the dawn of re-deem-ing grace,}

Sleep in heav-en-ly peace, Sleep in heav-en-ly peace.
Christ, the Sav-ior, is born! Christ the Sav-ior is born!
Je-sus, Lord, at Thy birth, Je-sus, Lord, at Thy birth.

No. 279   Away In A Manger

Martin Luther

1. A-way in a man-ger, No crib for a-bed, The lit-tle Lord
2. The cat-tle are low-ing, The Ba-by a-wakes, But lit-tle Lord
3. Be near me, Lord Je-sus, I ask Thee to stay Close by me for-

Je-sus Laid down is sweet head; The stars in the sky Looked
Je-sus, No cry-ing He makes; I love Thee, Lord Je-sus! Look
ev-er, And love me, I pray; Bless all the dear chil-dren In

Away In A Manger

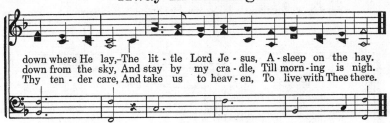

down where He lay,—The lit-tle Lord Je-sus, A-sleep on the hay.
down from the sky, And stay by my cra-dle, Till morn-ing is nigh.
Thy ten-der care, And take us to heav-en, To live with Thee there.

No. 280 While Shepherds Watched Their Flocks

Naham Tate

George F. Handel

1. While shep-herds watched their flocks by night, All seat-ed
2. "Fear not!" said He; for might-y dread Had seized their
3. To you, in Da-vid's town, this day Is born, of
4. All glo-ry be to God on high, And to the

on the ground, The an-gel of the Lord came down,
trou-bled mind, Glad ti-dings of great joy I bring,
Da-vid's line, The Sav-ior, who is Christ the Lord;
earth be peace: Good-will hence-forth from heav'n to men,

And glo-ry shone a-round, And glo-ry shone a-round.
To you and all man-kind, To you and all man-kind.
And this shall be the sign: And this shall be the sign.
Be-gin and nev-er cease, Be-gin and nev-er cease.

Ring the Bells

J. S. Davis & J. P. L.

J. P. Lane
Luther G. Presley

1. Ring,   O ring the bells,   The mer-ry bells
   Ring, O ring,   ring, O ring the bells,   Merry, merry bells;
2. Ring,   O ring the bells,   The mer-ry bells
   Ring, O ring,   ring, O ring the bells,   Merry, merry bells;

of Christmas time,   Toll,   O toll the theme,
   bells of Christmas time,   Toll, O toll,   toll, O toll the theme
of Christmas time,   Sad,   O sad the heart
   bells of Christmas time,   Sad, O sad,   sad, O sad the heart

So full of love   and grace sublime;
   Full of love and grace,   love and grace sublime;
That never hears   their soothing chime;
   Nev-er, nev-er hears,   nev-er hears their chime;

Deep   within our hearts   The swelling tones
Deep, so deep,   deep within our hearts,   Ever swelling tones
Let   the tones be fraught   With gladsome news,
Let, O let,   let the tones be fraught,   With the gladsome news,

Ring the Bells

Ring the Bells

chimes;
with their silv'ry chimes;   Sweet, O sweet the song
Sweet,O sweet,   sweet,O sweet the song,

Of ho - ly love
Song of ho - ly love,   their mu-sic tells,
love their music tells,

Toll - - - ing us a strain,
Toll - ing us,   toll - ing us a strain,   From realms a-

bove,
From the realms a - bove,   O Christmas bells.
bells,glad Christmas bells.

Coda

Ring the bells, Ring the bells, Ring the bells, Ring the Christmas bells.

No. 282 Baby Jesus

Kathryn Blackburn Peck Chorus- L. G. P. Faith Chambers Wilson

Softly

1. Ba - by Je - sus went to sleep On a bed of hay;
2. Mother Ma - ry tucked Him in, Warmed His ti - ny feet,

Cho. Sleep, sleep, ba - by sleep, Sleep ba - by sleep,

In a man - ger soft and deep Ba - by Je - sus lay.
Sang a lull - a - by to Him, "Sleep, my ba - by, sleep."

In a man - ger soft and deep, Sleep, ba - by, sleep.

No. 283 LITTLE BABY IN THE MANGER, I LOVE YOU

C. B. A. Carrie B. Adams

1. Lit - tle Ba - by in the man - ger, I love you, Ly - ing there, to
2. Lit - tle Ba - by down from heav - en, I love you, By the Fa - ther
3. Lit - tle Ba - by meek and low - ly, I love you, Son of God so

earth a stran - ger, I love you; Wise men saw the star, and an-swered,
to us giv - en, I love you; Star of hope for ev - 'ry na - tion,
pure and ho - ly, I love you; Won - der - ful in grace and pow - er,

I love you, Shep-herds heard the an - gels say - ing, I love you.
I love you, An - gels gave Thee ad - o - ra - tion, I love you.
I love you, Shar - on's Rose, the sweet-est flow - er, I love you.

No. 284 — Listen To The Bells

Luther G. Presley, owner., Pangburn, Ark. 1926.

L. G. P.

Luther G. Presley

1. Lis - ten to the mer-ry christmas bells, Ring-ing ev-'ry-where;
2. Glo - ry in the high-est peace on earth, Let your voic-es ring;
3. O'er the lit-tle town of Beth-le-hem, See the great bright Star;
   ring-ing ev-'ry-where;

Won-der-ful the news their peal-ing tells, Bless-ings and good cheer.
Sing a-bout the bless-ed Sav-ior's birth, He is Lord and King.
Point-ing out the place to those wise men, Com-ing from a-far.
Bless-ings and good cheer.

In a low-ly man-ger Christ is born, Oh, re-joice and sing;
Bring-ing light and gladness, peace, good cheer, To earth's lone-ly dells;
Won-der-ful Re-deem-er of the world, In a man-ger born;
re-joice and sing;

Join in Ser-aph song this christ-mas morn, To the new-born King.
O - ver all the land to-day we hear, Mer-ry christ-mas bells.
Let the news of glad-ness now be hurled, On this christmas morn.
new born King.

Chorus

Lis-ten to the bells, Lis-ten to the bells,
Glad christmas bells, Glad christmas bells,

Listen To The Bells

O - ver all the earth this christ-mas day, How their mu - sic swells;
rings and swells;

Lis - ten to the bells, Lis - ten to the bells,
Glad christmas bells, Glad christmas bells,

Driv-ing care and sad-ness all a-way, Mer - ry christ-mas bells.
Mer-ry christ-mas bells.

No. 285   Enough For Me

E. A. H.   Rev. E. A. Hoffman

1. O love sur-pass-ing knowl-edge! O grace, so full and free!
2. O won-der-ful sal-va-tion! From sin He makes me free!
3. O blood of Christ, so pre-cious, Poured out on Cal-va-ry!

Cho.- And that's e-nough for me, O that's e-nough for me:

D.C.

I know that Je - sus saves me, And that's e-nough for me.
I feel the sweet as-sur-ance, And that's e-nough for me.
I feel the cleans-ing pow-er, And that's e-nough for me.

I know that Je - sus saves me, And that's e-nough for me.

No. 286   Merry Christmas

L. G. P.

Luther G. Presley

1. Mer - - ry Christmas, greetings and good cheer, Wel - - come,
2. this is just for you,
3. Mer-ry, mer-ry Christmas, say it with a smile, Welcome, welcome,

welcome, we are glad you're here; San - ta Claus is com-ing,
tell you what to do; Pack a - way your troubles,
welcome, in the good old style; Join us ev - 'ry-bod - y,

nev - er fails to call, Mer - - ry Christmas to one and all.
hang them on the wall, whether great or small, Mer-ry, mer - ry

FINE

CHORUS

Mer - - ry Christmas, Sleigh-bells in the snow, Mer - - ry Christmas,
Mer-ry, mer-ry   Mer-ry, merry

D.S.

fac - es all a-glow; You are more than welcome to our fes-tive hall,

No. 287 Remember Me

Thos. J. Farris

No. 288 My Mother's Bible

Charlie D. Tillman
J. R. Baxter, Jr.

M. B. Williams

1. There's a dear and pre-cious book, tho it's worn and fad-ed now, Which re-
2. As she read the stor-ies o'er of those might-y men of old And of
3. Then she read of Je-sus' love as He blest the chil-dren dear, How He
4. Well, those days are past and gone but their mem'ry lin-gers still, And the

calls those hap-py days of long a-go, When I stood at moth-er's knee with her
Jos-eph and of Dan-iel and their tri'ls; Of that lit-tle Da-vid bold who be-
suf-fered, bled and died up-on the tree; Of His heav-y load of care, then she
dear old book each day has been my guide; And I seek to do His will, as my

hand up-on my brow, And I heard her voice in gen-tle tones and low.
came a king at last And of Sa-tan and his man-y wick-ed wiles.
dried my flow-ing tears With her kiss-es as she said it was for me.
moth-er taught me then And ev-er in my heart His word a-bide.

D. S.—walk the nar-row way That leads at last to that bright home a-bove.

Chorus

Bless-ed book, pre-cious book, On thy dear old tearstained
Bless-ed book, pre-cious book,

D. S.

leaves I love to look; Thou art sweet-er day by day as I
I love to look;

No. 289

Sweetest Mother

Will M. Ramsey
and Clyde Williams

1. She's a lit-tle old fash-ioned, that sweet moth-er of mine, There are
2. She's a lit-tle old fash-ioned, that sweet moth-er of mine, Tho
3. She's a lit-tle old fash-ioned, she stays close-ly at home, So

man-y whose beau-ty will my moth-er's out-shine; She's a lit-tle old
e-ven her plain-ness now my heartstrings en-twine; Oth-er hands may be
calm and con-tent-ed al-tho oth-ers may roam; And in ten-der young

D.S.- There's a glo-ry a-

fash-ioned as I plain-ly can see, But she is for-ev-er sweet-est
whit-er but none oth-er so dear, For they smoothed my pil-low for
child-hood 'twas a shel-ter for me, And she who so graced it, dear-est

round her, God a-bides it may be, And she is for-ev-er sweet-est

FINE CHORUS

moth-er to me. She's a lit-tle old fash-ioned, but she's sweet-er each
man-y a year.
ev-er shall be.

moth-er to me.

D.S.

day, I a-dore her plain fea-tures and her thin locks of gray;

Tell Mother I'll be There

C. M. F.

Charles M. Fillmore

1. When I was but a lit-tle child how well I rec-ol-lect
2. Tho I was oft-en way-ward, she was al-ways kind and good;
3. When I be-came a prod-i-gal, and left the old roof-tree,
4. One day a mes-sage came to me, it bade me quick-ly come

How I would grieve my mother with my fol-ly and neg-lect; And
So pa-tient, gen-tle, lov-ing, when my ways were rough and rude; My
She al-most broke her lov-ing heart in mourn-ing aft-er me; And
If I would see my moth-er ere the Sav-ior took her home; I

now that she has gone to heav'n I miss her ten-der care: O Sav-ior, tell my
childhood griefs and trials she would gladly with me share: O Sav-ior, tell my
day and night she prayed to God to keep me in His care: O Sav-ior, tell my
promised her, be-fore she died, for heav-en to pre-pare: O Sav-ior, tell my

Rit.

moth-er I'll be there!
I'll be there!

Chorus

Tell mother I'll be there in answer to her pray'r;

This message, bless-ed Sav-ior, to her bear! Tell mother I'll be there, heav'n's

Tell Mother I'll be There

Rit.

joys with her to share: Yes, tell my dar-ling mother I'll be there!

I'll be there!

No. 291 ## Shake Hands with Mother Again

W. A. B.

W. A. Berry

1. If I should be liv-ing when Je - sus comes And could know the day
2. I'd like to say "Moth-er, this is your boy, You left when you
3. There's coming a time when I can go home To meet my
4. There'll be no more sor-row or pain to bear In that home be-

and the hour, I'd like to be stand-ing at moth-er's tomb
went a - way; And now my dear moth-er it gives me great joy
loved ones up there; There I can see Je - sus up - on His throne
yond the sky; O glo - ri - ous tho't when we all get there,

:S: **Fine** **Chorus**

When Je - sus comes in His pow'r.
To see you a - gain to - day." 'Twill be a won-der-ful hap - py day
In that bright ci - ty so fair.
We nev - er will say "good-by."

D.S.-"Shake hands with mother again."

D.S.

Up there on the gold-en strand; When I can hear Je-sus my Sav - ior say,

No. 292 Mother's Prayers Have Followed Me.

Lizzie DeArmond.

B. D. Ackley.

M. 60 = ♩

1. I grieved my Lord from day to day, I scorned His love so full and
2. O'er des-ert wild, o'er moun-tain high, A wan-der-er I chose to
3. He turned my dark-ness in-to light, This bless-ed Christ of Cal-va-

free, And tho' I wan-dered far a-way, My moth-er's
be; A wretch-ed soul, con-demned to die, Still moth-er's
ry! I'll praise His name both day and night, That moth-er's

CHORUS.

pray'rs have fol-lowed me. I'm com-ing home, I'm com-ing

home, To live my wast-ed life a-new, For moth-er's

pray'rs have fol-lowed me, Have fol-lowed me the whole world through.

No. 293 If I Could Hear My Mother Pray Again

James Rowe

J. W. Vaughan, owner

J. W. Vaughan

1. How sweet and hap-py seem those days of which I dream, When mem-o-
2. She used to pray that I on Je-sus would re-ly, And al-ways
3. With-in the old home-place, her pa-tient, smil-ing face Was al-ways
4. Her work on earth is done, the life-crown has been won, And she will

ry re-calls them now and then! And with what rap-ture sweet my
walk the shin-ing gos-pel way; So trust-ing still His love I
spread-ing com-fort, hope and cheer; And when she used to sing to
be at rest with Him a-bove; And some glad morn-ing, she I

FINE

wea-ry heart would beat, If I could hear my moth-er pray a-gain.
seek that home a-bove, Where I shall meet my moth-er some glad day.
her e-ter-nal King, It was the songs the an-gels loved to hear.
know will wel-come me To that e-ter-nal home of peace and love.

D.S.-so much to me, If I could hear my moth-er pray a-gain.

CHORUS

If I could hear my moth-er pray a-gain, If I could
If I could on-ly If I could on-ly
If I could on-ly hear

D.S.

hear her ten-der voice as then! So glad I'd be, 'twould mean
hap-py I should
So hap-py I should be

No. 294   Mother's Way

A. D. W.   A. D. Wall

1. I'm fol-low-ing Je-sus and trust-ing His love,   I'm sure I shall meet my dear moth-er a-bove;   She taught me to love Him, she taught me to pray,   And now I am walk-ing in moth-er's bright way.

2. I know it will lead me to mansions of light—   A beau-ti-ful ci-ty that nev-er knows night;   There moth-er will meet me with sweet smil-ing face,   And I shall be glad that I trust-ed God's grace.

3. She lov-ing-ly told me of pit-falls and snares,   And prom-ised to help me a-long by her prayers;   And O I am sure her sweet pleadings were heard,   Be-cause I am led by the in-fi-nite Word.

4. O moth-ers, be true to your dear ones, I pray,   Be sure to point out the bright, heav-en-ly way;   In-struct them to fol-low and teach them to love,   That they may serve Je-sus and meet you a-bove.

Chorus

She taught me how to love the Lord, And how to strive for life's re-ward; She taught me how

Mother's Way

to trust and pray,
to trust and pray,
And now I walk
And now I walk
in mother's way.

No. 295   What a Friend

Joseph Scriven   Charles C. Converse

1. What a friend we have in Je - sus, All our sins and griefs to bear!
2. Have we tri - als and temp - ta - tions? Is there trou - ble an - y - where?
3. Are we weak and heav - y la - den, Cumbered with a load of care?—

What a priv - i - lege to car - ry Ev - 'ry-thing to God in pray'r!
We should nev - er be dis - cour-aged, Take it to the Lord in pray'r.
Pre-cious Sav - ior, still our ref - uge,—Take it to the Lord in pray'r.

O what peace we oft - en for - feit, O what need-less pain we bear,
Can we find a friend so faith - ful, Who will all our sor-rows share?
Do thy friends despise, for - sake Thee? Take it to the Lord in pray'r;

All be-cause we do not car - ry Ev - 'ry-thing to God in pray'r!
Je - sus knows our ev - 'ry weak-ness, Take it to the Lord in pray'r.
In His arms He'll take and shield thee, Thou wilt find a sol - ace there

No. 296 ANCHORED IN LOVE DIVINE

Rearranged expressly for V. O. Stamps, by A. M. Pace.

James Rowe **Howard E. Smith**

Bass Solo

1. Fear-ing the storm no more, Dread-ing no rock or shoal,
2. Bil - lows may swell and roll, Fierce-ly the storm may beat,
3. Here I will rest with Him, Je - sus my Sav-iour dear,

Hear-ing no breakers roar, Peace-ful is now my soul.
Safe will remain my soul Here in His ref - uge sweet,
Till thro' the shadows dim Life's end-less morn ap-pear;

O - ver my wand'ring days I shall no more re - pine;
All thro' the night I see Homelights that brightly shine,
Then on the hap - py shore, Where homes e-ter - nal shine,

rit.

Sing-ing to Je - sus a car-ol of praise, I'm anchored in love di - vine.
All will be well till the morning with me, I'm anchored in love di - vine.
Songs I shall sing in His praise ev-er-more, Still anchored in love di - vine.

CHORUS

Anchored in love di - vine, Je - sus at last is mine,

ANCHORED IN LOVE DIVINE

Allegretto.   *rit.*

Wondrously blest in the hav-en of rest, Anchored in love di - vine.

Coda after last stanza. Andante.

I'm an - chored safe in love di - vine.

No. 297   My Jesus, I Love Thee

London Hymn Book.   A. J. GORDON.

1. My Je - sus, I love Thee, I know Thou art mine; For Thee all the
2. I love Thee be-cause Thou hast first lov - ed me, And pur-chased my
3. I'll love Thee in life, I will love Thee in death, And praise Thee as
4. In man-sions of glo - ry and end - less de - light, I'll ev - er a-

fol - lies of sin I re-sign; My gra-cious Re - deem - er, my
par - don on Cal - va - ry's tree; I love Thee for wear - ing the
long as Thou lend - est me breath, And say when the death - dew lies
dore Thee in heav - en so bright; I'll sing with the glit - ter - ing

Sav - iour art Thou; If ev - er I loved Thee, my Je - sus, 'tis now.
thorns on Thy brow; If ev - er I loved Thee, my Je - sus, 'tis now.
cold on my brow; "If ev - er I loved Thee, my Je - sus, 'tis now."
crown on my brow; "If ev - er I loved Thee, my Je - sus, 'tis now."

Heaven's Jubilee

G. T. Speer

1. Some glad morn-ing we shall see Je-sus in the air, Com-ing af - ter
2. Seems that now I al-most see all the saint-ed dead, Ris - ing for that
3. When with all that heav'n-ly host we be - gin to sing, Sing-ing in the

you and me, joy is ours to share; What re - joic - ing there will be
ju - bi - lee, that is just a - head; In the twink-ling of an eye,
Ho - ly Ghost, how the heav'ns will ring; Mil-lions there will join the song,

when the saints shall rise, Head-ed for that ju - bi-lee, yon-der in the skies.
changed with them to be, All the liv-ing saints to fly to that ju - bi-lee.
with them we shall be Prais-ing Christ thru a - ges long, heav-en's ju - bi-lee.

CHORUS

Oh, what sing-ing, Oh, what shout-ing,
What a day of sing - ing, sing-ing, what a day of shout-ing, shout-ing,

On that hap - py morn-ing when we all shall rise;
when we all shall glad - ly rise;

Heaven's Jubilee

Oh, what glo - ry, Hal - le - lu - jah!
What a day of glo - ry, glo - ry, Glo - ry hal - le - lu - jah! glo - ry!

When we meet our bless-ed Sav - ior in the skies.
Sav - ior yon - der in the skies.

No. 299 Let The Lower Lights Be Burning

P. P. B.　　　　　　　Matt. 5:16　　　　　　P. P. Bliss

1. Bright-ly beams our Fa-ther's mer-cy, From His light-house ev - er-more
2. Dark the night of sin has set-tled, Loud the an - gry bil-lows roar;
3. Trim your fee-ble lamp, my broth-er; Some poor sail - or tem-pest tossed,

FINE

But to us He gives the keep-ing Of the lights a - long the shore.
Ea - ger eyes are watch-ing, long-ing, For the lights a - long the shore.
Try-ing now to make the har - bor, In the dark-ness may be lost.

D.S.- Some poor faint-ing, strug-gling sea-man, You may res - cue, you may save.

CHORUS　　　　　　　　　　　　　　　　　　　　　D.S.

Let the low - er lights be burn-ing! Send a gleam a-cross the wave!

No. 300   That Glad Reunion Day

A. M. P.

Adger M. Pace

1. There will be a hap-py meet-ing in heav-en I know,
2. There with-in the ho-ly cit-y we'll sing and re-joice,
3. When we live a mil-lion years in that won-der-ful place,

When we see the ma-ny loved ones we've known here be-low,
Prais-ing Christ the bless-ed Sav-iour with heart and with voice,
Bask-ing in the love of Je-sus, be-hold-ing His face,

Gath-er on the bless-ed hill-tops with hearts all a-glow,
Tell Him how we came to love Him and make Him our choice,
It will seem but just a mo-ment of prais-ing His grace,

D.S. - There with all the ho-ly an-gels and loved ones to stay,

FINE

That will be a glad re-un-ion day.

That will be a glad re-un-ion day.

CHORUS

Glad day, a
That will be a hap-py day, yes, a

D.S.

won-der-ful day, Glad day, a glo-ri-ous day;
won-der-ful day, That will be a hap-py day, yes, a glo-ri-ous day;

Copyright, 1940, Adger M. Pace. owner.

No. 301

The Love Of God

F. M. L.

F. M. Lehman
Arr. by Claudia Lehman Mays

1. The love of God is great-er far Than tongue or pen can ev-er tell;
2. When hoar-y time shall pass a-way, And earth-ly thrones and king-doms fall;
3. Could we with ink the o-cean fill, And were the skies of parch-ments made;

It goes be-yond the high-est star, And reach-es to the low-est hell;
When men who here re-fuse to pray, On rocks and hill and moun-tains call;
Were ev-'ry stalk on earth a quill, And ev-'ry man a scribe by trade;

The guilt-y pair, bowed down with care, God gave His Son to win;
God's love, so sure, shall still en-dure, All meas-ure-less and strong;
To write the love of God a-bove Would drain the o-cean dry;

His err-ing child He rec-on-ciled, And par-doned from his sin.
Re-deem-ing grace to Ad-am's race– The saints' and an-gels' song.
Nor could the scroll con-tain the whole, Tho' stretched from sky to sky.

Chorus

Oh, love of God, how rich and pure! How meas-ure-less and strong!
It shall for-ev-er-more en-dure– The saints and an- (Omit) gels song.

No. 302   Maybe It's You, Maybe It's Me

Arr.

Arr. Otis Deaton

1. Some-one will get a bless-ing as promised by the Lord, Some-one will then re-
2. Some-one will be in sor-row and tears will start to fall, No comfort, peace nor
3. Some-one will die to-mor-row, as man - y have to-day, This life is so un-

joice and hap-py be; Some-one will be heart-bro-ken and cry-ing mournful-ly,
hap-pi-ness they'll see; Some-one will have their troubles, be filled with miser - y,
cer-tain, we can see; Some-one the call will an-swer, we know not who 'twill be,

FINE CHORUS

May-be it's you and then, may-be it's me. May-be it's you and

then, may-be it's me Who'll be the next to face e-ter-ni-ty;

D.S.

When the day has come and gone, He will take some-bod - y home,

No. 303   Jesus Passed By

Copyright, 1953, by Marvin P. Dalton
Assigned to Tennessee Music & Printing Company

M. P. D.   Marvin P. Dalton

legato

1. There is a sto - ry of long a - go,   Men roamed in dark-ness
2. Men found com-pas - sion, hun - gry were fed,   Some saw their loved ones
3. One day a sin - ner, I found re - lief,   Gone was my bur - den.

no where to go;   One day the scene changed, they ceased to cry,
bro't from the dead;   They found great comfort came from on high.
gone was my grief;   An - gels were sing-ing, and so was I,

CHORUS

There was a rea - son, Je - sus passed by.   Glo - ry and hon - or
be to the King, Shout hal - le - lu - jah, make praises ring;   Look to the
fu-ture home in the sky,   There is a rea - son, Je - sus passed by.

No. 304   I Want to Know More About My Lord

L. R. A.   in "Golden Steps"   Lee Roy Abernathy

1. While trav'ling thru this world of sor-row, I'm on my way to glo-ry
2. I'm glad I know the bless-ed Sav-ior, For thru His blood He set me
3. He promised when His soul as-cend-ed, I'm com-ing back, the Lord did

land; I'll not turn back, for some to-morrow, My tri-als here I'll un-der-
free; Tho rough the road, I shall not wav-er, For some glad day His face I'll
say; If on His prom-ise you've depended, On wings of love you'll soar a-

Chorus

stand. I want to know more   a-bout my Je-sus,
see.
way.   I want to know more   yes, I do,

I want to know more   a-bout my Lord;
Yes,   I want to know more   my blessed Lord;

I want to know more   a-bout that mansion,
          I want to know more   heav-en-ly man-

I Want to Know More About My Lord

I'm gon-na re-ceive as my re-ward;
sion, I'm gon-na re-ceive my rich re-ward;

I want to know more a-bout that homeland,
I want to know more won-der-ful home-

I mean to go there, some day, somehow;
land, O, I mean to go there, some day, somehow;

And af-ter I reach that heav-en-ly cit-y,
And af-ter I reach heav-en-ly cit-

I mean to know more than I know now.
y, yes, I'm gonna know more, I'm gonna know more than I know now.

No. 305

Heavenly Love

Title suggested by Bill Baker, Louisville, Ky.

V. B. E.

V. B. (Vep) Ellis

1. Heav - en - ly love.................... was all that could
2. Trou - bles of earth (repeat words of soprano) so of - ten o'er-
3. When I shall stand.................... at Jor - dan's dark

help me,.................... I was a - stray.................... so
take me,.................... Bur - dens of life.................... with
riv - er,.................... Shad - ows of night.................... are

sad and a - lone;.................... I looked a -
heart - ache and care;.................... Heav - en - ly
gath - 'ring a - bove;.................... There is a

bove.................... my bur - dens all left me,....................
love.................... will nev - er for - sake me,....................
pow'r.................... I know will de - liv - er,....................

Now I can say,.................... "Heav - en's my home"....................
Fill - ing my need,.................... Je - sus is there....................
Heav - en - ly love,.................... heav - en - ly love.

Heavenly Love

CHORUS

Heav - en - ly love, the love of my
Heav - en - ly love the

Lord, Lift - ing a - bove for
love of my Sav - ior, Lift - ing a - bove

He is my sword and shield; Giv - ing me light in
my sword and shield; Giv - ing me light

dark - ness of night, Heav - en - ly
in dark - ness of night,

love, heav - en - ly love.
Heav - en - ly love, heav - en - ly love.

No. 306 Land Where Living Waters Flow

Copyright, 1950, by Statesmen Quartet
in "Souvenir Album"

Mosie Lister   Mosie Lister

1. Some glad day my soul will fly, 'way up high in the sky;
2. Far a - bove this vale of tears, doubts and fears, home ap - pears;

Far a - bove this land of grief and woe;   With my Lord I'll
Home where I have longed so much to go;   Soon on wings of

fly a - way, on that day, hap - py day, To that land where
love I'll rise, to the prize in the skies,

Chorus

liv - ing wa - ters flow.   That land where liv - ing
        O that land   where liv - ing

wa - ters flow, My soul is long - ing to be there;
wa - ters flow, My soul is long - ing to be there; And

Land Where Living Waters Flow

And some glad day I know I'll go To live for-
some glad day I know I'll go To live for-

ev - er in the air. 'Tis a love - ly land, won - der land,
ev - er in the air.

where the an - gels sing, 'Round the throne, shin - ing throne, prais - ing

heav - en's King; And some glad day I know I'll go
And some glad day I know I'll go

To that land where liv - ing wa - ters flow.

No. 307   Peace Like A River

W. B. Walbert

James D. Walbert

1. Peace like a riv - er,
Peace like a riv - er, peace like a riv - er
2. Peace gent - ly flow - ing,
Peace gent - ly flow - ing, peace gent - ly flow - ing,

Flows thru my soul;
Flows thru my soul, flows thru my soul; I've been for -
Sweet and di - vine,
Sweet and di - vine, sweet and di - vine; Gives the as -

giv - en,
I've been for - giv - en, cleansed and made whole, cleansed and made whole.
sur - ance
gives the as - sur - ance Je - sus is mine, Je - sus is mine.

Chorus

Peace, peace,
Peace like a riv-er so gently is flowing, how sweet to my soul is this marvelous peace,

Sweet peace, God's peace;
Sweeter and sweeter each day it is grow - ing, like billows of glo - ry, it nev-er shall cease;

Peace Like A River

No. 308

THE MASTER OF THE STORM.

James Rowe.   J. Porter Thomason.

1. Out on the o-cean of life we sail, Battered by ma-ny a
2. Wrecks we are see-ing from day to day— Poor broken ves-sels, a-
3. True to our Pi-lot we all shall be, Whether a storm-y or

rag - ing gale, Yet we are sure that we shall pre-vail, No
long the way; No one to pi-lot their ships have they; And
peace - ful sea; Al - ways so help-ful and sweet is He, And

storm can His ship o'er-whelm..... Bil-lows may threaten and winds may blow,
so they are sink-ing fast....... Je - sus would pi-lot their ves - sel, too,
bless-ing us ev - er-more...... Soon we shall meet Him up-on the strand

Cour - age and faith we shall al - ways show; Noth-ing can harm us as
Com - fort and give to them cour - age new; If they be-lieved Him and
Of the e - ter-nal and hap - py land, Then we shall praise Him in

on we go, For Je - sus is at the helm.(at the helm.)
would be true, Their tri - als would soon be past.(soon be past.)
cho - rus grand With those who have reached the shore.(reached the shore.)

CHORUS.

He is the Mas-ter of wind and tide; Safe-ly the bil-lows His
He rules temp-est and tide; Ev - er safe His

ship will ride; In - to the har-bor at last it will glide, Where
ves - sel will ride; Safe-ly

we shall be wondrously blest; And so with our Pi-lot we sail a-
for-ev-er; And so we're sail-ing a-

long, Safe from the storm and from all things wrong; Soon we shall
long, We are safe from things that are wrong; Singing

en - ter the har-bor of song—The ha - ven of end-less rest........
joy and rest.

No. 309   Help Me Lord, to Stand

B. F.

Byron Faust

1. Help me oh, Lord, to do Thy will, hum-bly now I pray, Help me, to
2. Help me when I am prone to stray from Thy bless-ed fold, Help me to
3. Help me to walk the nar-row road, Lord, I hum-bly pray, Help me to

Thee, my serv-ice give, all a-long my way; That I, oh, Lord, may
walk in Thine own way, to the gates of gold; And when I'm bur-dened
bear some oth-ers load, struggling in the way; Help me to build up-

live for Thee, do Thy blest command, When try-ing moments come to me,
down with care, hold me by Thy hand, And when my load is hard to bear,
on the Rock, not up-on the sand, And when shall come the tempest shock,

CHORUS.

help me Lord to stand. Help me, oh, Lord, to stand each
Help me, oh, Lord, to stand each

shock, That comes a-long my way;
tem-pest shock, That comes a-long my way, a-long my way;

Help Me Lord, to Stand

Help me to stand up-on the rock,
Help me to stand up-on the sol-id Rock,

And live for Thee each day. Be Thou
And live for Thee each day, for Thee each day. Be Thou my

my guid-ing Star, my guid-ing Star, And hold me by Thy
guid-ing Star, And hold me by Thy

hand, yes, by Thy hand; And when I face the judg-ment
hand; And when I face the judgment,

bar, Help me, oh, Lord, to stand.
judgment bar, Help me, oh, Lord, to stand, to brave-ly stand.

No. 310 — My God Is Real

K. M.   Kenneth Morris

1. There are some things ...... I may not know, ... There are some
2. Some folk may doubt, ... some folk may scorn, ... All can go
3. I can-not tell ...... just how you felt ...... When Je-sus

plac-es I can't go, But I am sure ....
on and leave me a-lone, But as for me ....
took your sins a-way, But since that day ....

of this one thing .... That God is real for I can
I'll take God's part, ... And God is real for I can
yes, since that hour .... God has been real for I can

feel Him deep within.
feel Him in my heart.
feel His ho-ly pow'r.

CHORUS

My God is real, real in my
My God is real,

My God Is Real

soul, My God is real for He has washed and made me
real in my soul, Real washed

whole; His love for me is like pure gold,
made me whole; His love for me is like pure gold,

My God is real for I can feel Him in my soul.
Real feel ransomed soul.

No. 311 ## I Am Bound For the Promised Land

Rev. Samuel Stennet   Rev. 21 : 2   Arr. by Rev. E. M. Parnum

1. On Jordan's storm-y banks I stand, And cast a wish-ful eye,
2. O'er all those wide ex-tended plains Shines one e-ter-nal day;
3. When shall I reach that hap-py place, And be for-ev-er blest!

Cho.—I am bound for the promised land, I am bound for the promised land;

'Tward Ca-naan's fair and hap-py land, Where my pos-ses-sions lie.
There God the Son for-ev-er reigns, And scat-ters night a-way.
When shall I see my Fa-ther's face, And in His bos-om rest?

O who will come and go with me, I am bound for the prom-ised land.

No. 312   Jesus Paid It All

ARRANGEMENT COPYRIGHT, 1925, BY J. W. GAINES

Mrs. M. M. Hall   Arr. by J. W

1. I hear the Savior say, hear the Savior say, "Thy strength... in-deed is
1. I hear......... the Sav-ior say, "Thy strength indeed is small,
2. Lord, now indeed I find, now indeed I find, Thy pow'r,..... and Thine a-
2. Lord, now......... in-deed I find, Thy pow'r, and Thine alone,
3. For nothing good have I, nothing good have I, Whereby...... Thy grace to
3. For noth - - - ing good have I, Whereby Thy grace to claim—
4. And when, before the throne, when before the throne, I stand....... in Him com-
4. And when,........ be-fore the throne, I stand in Him complete,

small, Child of weakness, watch and pray, ev-er watch and pray,
strength indeed is small, Child of weak - - ness, watch and pray,
lone, Can change the leper's spots, change the lep-er's spots,
pow'r, and Thine a-lone, Can change.......... the lep-er's spots,
claim— I'll wash my garments white, wash my garments white,
sav - ing grace to claim—I'll wash........... my garments white,
plete, "Je-sus died my soul to save," "died my soul to save,"
stand in Him complete. "Je-sus died............. my soul to save,"

CHORUS.

Find in Me Thine all in all."(thine all in all.") Je-sus paid it all,
And.... melt the heart of stone. (the heart of stone.)
In the blood of Calv'ry's Lamb. (of Calv'ry's Lamb.)
My.... lips shall still re-peat. (shall still re-peat.) Je - - sus paid it

Je-sus paid it all, All to Him I owe, I owe;....
all, All to Him I owe;....

He opened wide the cleansing fountain,

Jesus Paid It All

Sin had left a stain, a crim-son stain, He washed it white as snow.
Sin had left yes, white as snow.

313

Is It Well With Your Soul?

Copyright © 1966, by Stamps-Baxter Music & Printing Co.
All Rights Reserved. Printed in U. S. A.

James Rowe and
Alfred Matthews, Jr.

Virgil O. Stamps

1. 'Mid the toil and strife of this bus-y life, Is it well
2. Have you lost your sin, are you pure with-in?
3. Do you praise the love of the One a-bove?
4. Be pre-pared my friend when this life shall end, Is it well

with your soul? Are you liv-ing right, should you die to-night?
Are you at the side of the cru-ci-fied?
Will the crown be won and the Lord's "well done?"
with your soul? If you long-er wait, it may be too late,

D.S.- Are you liv-ing right, should you die to-night?

FINE CHORUS

Is it well with your soul?
Is it well   Is it well   Is it well

Is it well .... with your soul?

D.S.

with your soul,   Are you free, glad and whole?
with your soul,   Are you free,   glad and whole?

No. 314 I Bowed On My Knees And Cried, "Holy"

Arranged by Ben Speer

1. I dreamed I went to that cit-y called glo-ry, So bright and so fair, When I en-tered the gate I cried, "Ho-ly," The an-gels all met me there; They showed me from man-sion to man-sion, And oh, the sights I saw, But I said, "I want to see Je-sus, The

2. I tho't when I en-tered that cit-y, My friends knew me well, They showed me all thru heav-en, The scenes are too nu-m'rous to tell; They showed me A-bra-ham, I-saac, Ja-cob, Mark, Luke, and Tim-o-thy, But I said, "I want to give praise, To the

3. I tho't when I saw my Sav-iour, Oh! glo-ry to God! I just fell right down be-fore Him, Sing-ing, "Praise to the name of the Lord;" I bowed down and wor-shipped Je-ho-vah, My friend of Cal-va-ry, For I want-ed to give praise to Je-sus, For

I Bowed On My Knees And Cried, "Holy"

CHORUS

One who died for all.
One who died for me. Then I bowed on my
sav - ing a sin - ner like me.

knees and cried, "Ho - ly, Ho - ly, Ho - ly," I clapped my hands

Rit.

and sang, "Glo - ry, glo - ry to the Son of God."

No. 315   Whisper A Prayer

Unknown   Arr. by Mrs. Jas. Pate

1. Whis-per a prayer in the morn - ing, Whis-per a prayer at noon;
2. God answers prayer in the morn - ing, God an-swers prayer at noon;
3. Je - sus may come in the morn - ing, Je - sus may come at noon;

Whis-per a prayer in the eve - ning, To keep your heart in tune.
God an-swers prayer in the eve - ning, To keep your heart in tune.
Je - sus may come in the eve - ning, So keep your heart in tune.

No. 316   Jesus Paid it All

M. S. Shaffer   Stamps-Baxter Music and Ptg. Co., owners   Samuel W. Beazley

1. Gone is all my debt of sin, A great change is bro't within, And to live I
2. O   I hope to please Him now, Light of joy is on my brow, As at His dear
3. Sin-ner, not for me a-lone Did the Son of God a-tone; Your debt, too, He

now be-gin, Ris-en from the fall; Yet the debt I did not pay Some one
feet I bow, Safe with-in His love. Mak-ing His the debt I owed, Free-dom
made His own, On the cru-el tree. Come to Him with all your sin; Be as

died for me one day, Sweeping all the debt a-way, Je-sus paid it all.
true He has bestowed; So I'm sing-ing on the road To my home a-bove.
white as snow with-in; Full sal-va-tion you may win And re-joice with me.

Chorus Bass to predominate in power.

Je-sus died and paid it all, yes, On the cross of Cal-va-ry, O
Je-sus died and paid it On the cross of Cal-va-ry,

And my ston-y heart was melt-ed At His dy-ing, dy-ing call
And my heart was melt-ed At His dy-ing call;

Jesus Paid it All

O His heart in shame was brok-en On the tree for you and me, yes,
O His heart was brok - en On the tree for you and me,

And the debt, the debt is can-celled, Je-sus paid it, paid it all.
And the debt is can - celled, Je - sus paid it all.

No. 317   Jesus, Lover of my Soul

Charles Wesley   S. B. Marsh
                                                  Fine

1 Je - sus, lov - er of my soul,   Let me to Thy bos - om fly,
{ While the near-er wa - ters roll, While the tem-pest still is high!

2 Oth - er ref - uge have I none,   Hangs my help - less soul on Thee:
{ Leave, ah, leave me not a - lone, Still sup-port and com-fort me!

3 Thou, O Christ, art all I want;   More than all in Thee I find;
{ Raise the fall - en, cheer the faint, Heal the sick, and lead the blind.

4 Plenteous grace with Thee is found, Grace to cov - er all my sin;
{ Let the heal-ing streams a-bound,   Make and keep me pure with-in.

D. C.—Safe in - to the ha - ven guide, O re-ceive my soul at last!
D. C.—Cov-er my de - fense-less head   With the shad-ow of Thy wing.
D. C.—False and full of sin I am,   Thou art full of truth and grace.
D. C.—Spring Thou up with-in my heart, Rise to all e - ter - ni - ty.

                                                  D.C.

Hide me, O my Sav-ior, hide,   Till the storm of life is past;
All my trust on Thee is stayed,   All my help from Thee I bring;
Just and ho - ly is Thy name,   I am all un-right-eous-ness;
Thou of life the foun-tain art;   Free - ly let me take of Thee;

I'll Live In Glory

J. M. H.   J. M. Henson

1. I'd like to stay here longer than man's al-lot-ted days And watch the fleet-ing
2. I want to be of serv-ice a-long this pil-grim way And lead the lost to
3. The end I know is near-ing — by faith I look a-way To yon-der home su-

chang-es of life's un-e-ven ways, But if my Sav-ior calls me to
Je-sus as fer-vent-ly I pray; As day by day I trav-el I'll
per-nal— the land of end-less day; I'll cling to Him for-ev-er, and

that sweet home on high, I'll live with Him for-ev-er in Glo-ry by and by.
keep Him ev-er nigh, And live with Him for-ev-er in Glo-ry by and by.
look be-yond the sky, And spend the end-less a-ges in Glo-ry by and by.

CHORUS

O yes, I'll live in Glo-ry   by   and by, I'll tell and sing love's
          live in Glo-ry by and by,

sto-ry   there   on   high; There with my dear Re-deem-er   no
       tell love's sto-ry there on high;   there no

I'll Live In Glory

more to die, O yes, I'll live in glo-ry by and by.
nomoreto die, glo-ry by andby.

No. 319   'Tis The Old Ship of Zion

E. R.   Ernest Rippetoe

Chorus

'Tis the old ship of Zi - on, 'Tis the old ship of Zi - on,

'Tis the old ship of Zi - on, Get on board, get on board.

1. It has land-ed my old moth-er, It has land-ed my old moth-er,
2. It has land-ed my old fa-ther, It has land-ed my old fa-ther,
3. It has land-ed Paul and Si-las, It has land-ed Paul and Si-las,

It has land-ed my old moth-er, Get on board, get on board.
It has land-ed my old fa-ther, Get on board, get on board.
It has land-ed Paul and Si-las, Get on board, get on board.

No. 320   A Savior To Be Proud Of

James Rowe   Austin Hazelwood   Arr. V. O. Fossett

1. I am mak-ing known to oth-ers the Re-deem-er of my soul, God's e-
2. He is clos-er than a broth-er ev-'ry mo-ment of the day, And His
3. Where the an-gels sing His prais-es I shall wor-ship and a-dore, When on

ter-nal Son who to my res-cue came; I shall love Him and a-
love and good-ness ev-er are the same; "Where He leads me I will
earth no long-er I can spread His fame; Thru the a-ges I shall

dore Him while un-num-bered a-ges roll,
fol-low" what-so-ev-er be the way, He's a Sav-ior to be proud of,
praise Him and ex-alt Him ev-er-more,

CHORUS

bless His name! He's a Sav-ior to be proud of, bless His name! For, to

res-cue me, from glo-ry Je-sus came; He has died to set me free—now His

A Savior To Be Proud Of

grace is keep-ing me, He's a Sav - ior to be proud of, bless His name!

No. 321   How Firm A Foundation

George Keith

1. How firm a foun - da - tion, ye saints of the Lord, Is laid
2. "Fear not, I am with Thee, O be not dis-mayed, For I
3. "When thru fier - y tri - als thy path - way shall lie, My grace,
4. "E'en down to old age, all My peo - ple shall prove My sov -
5. "The soul that on Je - sus still leans for re - pose, I will

for your faith in His ex - cel-lent Word! What more can He say, than to
am thy God, I will still give thee aid; I'll strength-en thee, help thee, and
all - suf - fi - cient, shall be thy sup - ply; The flame shall not hurt thee, I
'reign, e - ter - nal, un-change-a - ble love; And when hoar - y hairs shall their
not, I will not de - sert to his foes; That soul, tho all hell should en -

you He hath said, To you who for ref - uge to Je - sus have fled?
cause thee to stand, Up - held by My gra-cious, om - nip - o - tent hand.
on - ly de - sign Thy dross to con-sume, and thy gold to re - fine.
tem - ples a - dorn, Like lambs they shall still in My bos - om be borne.
deav - or to shake, I'll nev - er, no nev - er no nev - er for-sake!"

No. 322 — Satisfied

Anna B. Steinhoff

J. W. C. Arr. by J. L. Moore

Bass Solo

1. Tho the sor-rows of life press me sore   And the stars of my hope seems to
2. Help me, Lord, still in hope to re-joice,   And be pa-tient when bit - ter - ly
3. O how per-fect the love, peace and home,   Of the souls who with loved ones a-

hide,   Still I trust thru the dark-ness and pain,   For I know   I shall
tried,   And be faith - ful e'en un - to the end,   And at last   I shall
bide   'Round the throne of the Sav-ior and King,   Thru whose blood they are

CHORUS

be sat - is - fied.   Sat - is - fied,   sat - is - fied,
be sat - is - fied.   Yes, sat - is - fied,   yes, sat - is - fied,
all sat - is - fied.

O my soul, thou shalt be sat - is - fied;   Sat - is - fied,
sat - is - fied;   Yes, sat - is - fied,

sat - is - fied,   O my soul, thou shalt be sat - is - fied.
yes, sat - is - fied,   sat - is - fied.

For Me

B. B. Edmiaston

Copyright, 1923, by Emmett S. Dean

Emmett S. Dean

Slowly

1. For me (the Lord prayed,) He prayed, (for re-lief,) For me, for
2. For me (He was slain,) He died (on the cross,)
3. For me (dead in sin,) He 'rose (from the grave,) for me,

me;......... A-lone, (His heart broke,) a-lone, (He bore grief,)
In shame (be-tween thieves,) in shame, (and deep loss,)
for me; With pow'r (sub-dued death,) with pow'r, (me to save,)

Chorus *Faster*

For me.......... for me.... .... Glo-ry to God! He's
for me. for me.

com-ing a-gain, Com-ing to earth for me;
He's com-ing for me;

King of all kings, my Sav-iour will reign, In all e-ter-ni-ty.

No. 324 All Hail The Power

Edward Perronet

Oliver Holden

1. All hail the pow'r of Je - sus' name! Let an - gels pros-trate fall!
2. Ye cho - sen seed of Is - rael's race, Ye ran-somed from the fall,
3. Let ev - 'ry kin - dred, ev - 'ry tribe, On this ter - res - trial ball,
4. O that with yon - der sa - cred throng We at His feet may fall!

Bring forth the roy - al di - a - dem,
Hail Him who saves you by His grace, And crown Him Lord of all!
To Him all maj - es - ty as - cribe,
We'll join the ev - er - last - ing song,

Bring forth the roy - al di - a - dem,
Hail Him who saves you by His grace, And crown Him Lord of all!
To Him all maj - es - ty as - cribe,
We'll join the ev - er - last - ing song,

Second Tune

William Shrubsole

1. All hail the pow'r of Jesus' name! Let angels prostrate fall! Bring forth the roy-

al di - a - dem, And crown Him, crown Him, crown Him, Crown Him Lord of all!

INDEX

(Heavenly Highway Hymns)

INDEX
(Heavenly Highway Hymns)

INDEX

(Heavenly Highway Hymns)

INDEX

(Heavenly Highway Hymns)